THE BOY
DAVID

With Best Wishes,

Marjorie Jackson

THE BOY
DAVID

MARJORIE JACKSON

In nature there's no blemish but the mind;
None can be call'd deform'd but the unkind.

WILLIAM SHAKESPEARE

BRITISH BROADCASTING CORPORATION

Dedicated to
the people of Glasgow
and the West of Scotland

Acknowledgement is due to the following for permission to reproduce photographs: 21, *Evening Times*, Glasgow; 22, 23, 24, 25, 26, 27, 28, 29 and 30, Desmond Wilcox. The remaining pictures were supplied by Ian and Marjorie Jackson.

Published by the British Broadcasting Corporation
35 Marylebone High Street London W1M 4AA

ISBN 0 563 20350 1 (hardback)
ISBN 0 563 20420 6 (paperback)

First published 1985

Typeset in 11/13pt Times Roman by
Phoenix Photosetting, Chatham
Printed in England by Mackays of Chatham Limited

CONTENTS

FOREWORD

Initially when my wife told me she was going to write a book about David I was sceptical. I was not sure that it was a good idea and I doubted her ability to organise such a project. I was confounded on both issues.

Although this seems just an account of David's unique story it is, in effect, much more. It is a commentary on human beings, on their compassion and on their frailties. It highlights a city – Glasgow, 'no mean city', home of street gangs, violence and religious intolerance, but with a heart which overflows with warmth and kindness for a good cause. It shows a country – Peru – where poverty, disease and crime is the stuff of daily life for a vast section of society. It transports us from there to a centre of ultra-sophisticated medical care in the American Midwest – the famous Mayo Clinic. Scattered throughout this, like fairy lights on a Christmas tree, are individuals who have lighted David's way by their understanding and unselfish caring.

With great effort, self sacrifice and much self doubt, the book has been produced. I am ashamed that I ever questioned Marjorie's ability to do this. It is a profoundly moving and educational document. Praise is given where it has been earned but there has been no hesitation to criticise, whether it be country, institution or individual, if they have shown intolerance. There is no doubt in my mind that this book will help to increase the understanding, not only of the individual with the deformity, but those with whom he lives. It will also cause many to stand back and look at their own prejudices and those of society. I hope it will be understood that the central theme of this book is the life story of every deformed child. They all suffer, yet they all show amazing courage in the face of multiple surgeries and the inevitable associated pain. Let us not forget, however, a very important point which, although not within the context of the book, is most relevant in relation to deformity. Children grow up and the attitude of the world hardens; let us not lose the compassion generated by the charm of youth. Understanding for the adult is even more important and a search for the inner man is a rewarding experience.

Although this is a tale of a brave little boy whom one cannot but fail to admire, it also fills us with some degree of pride and hope for the future. These feelings are inspired by the kindness of many hundreds or maybe thousands of people – young and old, rich and poor – who have contributed to David's story. Mankind is not all bad! I salute my wife!

Ian T. Jackson

PREFACE

The decision to tell the story of David was not made lightly or quickly: it was given a great deal of serious thought. My husband Ian and I knew that it would affect the whole family, including David, and his well-being is paramount.

The first weeks after David's arrival were very busy and filled with concern for his welfare. It took almost all my energy just to get through the day. I was my husband's office manager and secretary as well as caring for four children and running the home. As time passed, however, I began to realise what a unique experience we were having as a family. I knew I had to find time to record it so that in future years we could remember what David's coming meant to us.

In writing the book I have attempted to be as factual as possible, but I hope I have allowed you to come to know David as a real little boy. I hope too that you know a little about the two men – my husband and Dr Navarro – without whom there would be no story. It is important for them to be seen as they are: caring, compassionate, dedicated men who are subject to all the worries and doubts of any individual; who are able to admit that they are sometimes afraid in the light of the responsibility their work thrusts upon them. With the help of my husband, I have outlined how the reconstruction of David's face was planned and undertaken, slowly bit by bit, in more than fifty operations. David's courage in dealing with the pain resulting from surgery is matched by his humour when he regards his own progress. He is of course very special to us, but there are thousands of children with craniofacial defects who face the same type of surgery as David and who respond to it with the same brand of courage as he displays. If telling David's story helps to make people more aware of such children's problems, making our private lives public will have been worthwhile.

In 1977, the plight of 'The Boy David' triggered off a most amazing response to a child in need; because of it, we have been privileged to help David face his future with hope. Please continue to respond to other children in need and give them, too, the warmth of your caring and hope for their future.

I
THE ADVENTURE BEGINS

David, our little Peruvian Indian, is now a boy of several countries. Although he was born a Campa Indian in a remote area of the Andean jungle in Peru, if you ask him, he will tell you that he is Scottish! Of Peru he knows very little and remembers nothing, but of Glasgow, the city which took him to its heart and gave him hope for the future, he knows quite a lot. In his years of being in and out of hospital he has met a variety of people and has developed a typical pawky sense of Glaswegian-type humour. He has no difficulty at all in understanding the Glasgow patois, or indeed conversing in it. Although he lived in Spain for two winters the majority of his time there was spent in school and so the customs and culture of that country affected him little. The influence of Mary and Robert Rodriguez, and the quality of his life with them in a small village in southern Spain, however, was absolutely marvellous and, we hope, lasting. We would like very much for David to be able to spend time with them whenever circumstances and finance allow. Now he is living in a small town in the American Midwest and he is learning to adapt to yet another way of life.

Glasgow, the industrial if not the fiscal capital of Scotland, is large, grey and often gloomy, but it's my city and I love it. Ian and I were born and brought up in Glasgow and we attended the same school in the east end of the city. Ian's career in medicine began at Glasgow University and after his graduation there in 1959 his years of training were mainly undertaken at Glasgow Royal Infirmary, with a spell in Sweden and several other European countries. When the Regional Plastic Surgery Centre opened at Canniesburn Hospital in the north-west of Glasgow, this became his base and he worked there until we came to Minnesota. Because of the type of surgery in which he specialised he had strong links with the department of neurosurgery in the Southern General Hospital, and with the Centre for Rheumatic Diseases in Baird Street.

The people of Glasgow are renowned for their warm cheerfulness and optimism in a climate where long, dark periods with lots of rain are interrupted by gleams of sunshine. The population is a mixture of

9

Celts, Indians, Pakistanis, and others: in the streets Chinese restaurants stand shoulder to shoulder with 'Indo-Pak' eating houses, and the Glasgow palate is as accustomed to curries, biryanis, and chop suey, as it is to the traditional 'fish and chips'. Daily, children of different cultures work, eat and play together.

From Glasgow, in the heart of Scotland, came an overwhelmingly compassionate response to the plight of one small Indian boy from a country very different and very far away. This determination to help pulsed through the arterial systems of church, schools, and press and was so successful that not only did it provide the security we needed to help David, but it renewed our belief that still, in these times of much talked about violence and crime, people care. We have been given an unequivocal demonstration of the depth of that caring . . . but how did all this begin?

It was in Glasgow in April 1974 that my husband and I had dinner one evening with a plastic surgeon, Carlos Navarro, and his wife, Elvira, from Lima, the capital city of Peru. Dr Navarro was at that time attending a teaching course for plastic surgeons at Canniesburn Hospital. He and Ian had corresponded from time to time but they had not met until the time of this symposium in Glasgow. There was undoubtedly an immediate rapport between them and as a result the dinner was arranged. I was soon enjoying their open friendliness and infectious humour and understood Ian's willingness to give up some of our precious evening hours to spend time with them.

At first sight Carlos and Ian seemed an incompatible pair, as far as looks go! Carlos is very fair-skinned and has blond hair with reddish-coloured tints, much more typical of a Celt or Scandinavian than a South American. Ian, on the other hand, is dark-skinned and has dark hair. As was the fashion at this time his hair was rather long and he sported a 'viva Zapata' moustache. This diversity of looks led to complications later!

Dinner that evening in Glasgow was a somewhat leisurely affair and thus in a few hours of stimulating conversation we covered a varied range of topics. We found out that Carlos and Elvira have a family of three boys. They in turn learned that we have four children, three girls and one boy. They told us also of their love for the Scottish people and for Scotland, where they had always been treated with great courtesy and friendliness. They seemed to be enjoying Glasgow and it pleased us to realise that they had the ability to see behind the superficial grim façade of slums and sometimes violence, the warmth of its citizens who are quick to smile and to lend a helping hand.

We talked about Peru, too, of course. Ian and I have a fascination for the history of Peru and the Inca civilisation. We are intrigued by the mysterious mountain city of Machu Picchu and romantic names such as Cusco, Arequipa and Lake Titicaca, but our knowledge of modern Peru was scant in the extreme. Carlos and Elvira told us many things about their country and the different types of people to be found there. Lima is on sea-level where the climate is mild with no really cold weather and no rain. It is hard for a native of Scotland to imagine a city where it never rains! The Indian population of Lima is far greater than the white population and these people live mainly in very poor areas. They have had to adapt to city life in order to survive and in doing this have lost a great deal of their own unique and fascinating culture.

Inevitably economics, politics and the sytem of government were discussed and the social structure clarified. Unfortunately, in Peru as elsewhere in the past few years, the degree of unemployment has constantly risen. Many Peruvians find it extremely difficult to provide for themselves and their families.

As is the case when all enthusiastic surgeons meet, surgery is discussed – frequently it may be the only topic for an entire evening! That particular evening gave birth to the idea that at some time Ian should visit Peru and work with Carlos in Lima. Carlos, craftily taking advantage of the fact that Ian was always ready to help, was also playing on Ian's tremendous interest in the history of Peru. Together they explored the possibilities of trying to organise some teaching sessions and seminars for the younger surgeons in Lima. Carlos carefully explained the facilities which would be available and also talked about the difficulties peculiar to his situation.

I found all of this interesting and somewhat amusing – it sounded like many conversations we had had during similar evenings with other surgeons from other countries. Carlos spoke about his day-to-day clinical work and voiced his frustrations about certain aspects of his surgical practice. The main area in which he needed help in order to gain more experience was that of major facial deformity, an area of surgery in which Ian is highly-skilled and experienced. Carlos, a very careful and capable surgeon, experienced in the surgery of cleft lip and palate and many other reconstructive procedures, wished to learn more in the field of major craniofacial reconstruction to enable him to help his own people more effectively. Possibly the wine had had a mellowing effect and both men felt ready to conquer the world! To be serious, however, they felt that if they could operate on some cases together in Lima, and if Ian could be there for the immediate post-operative period, then Carlos could deal with any possible subsequent problems. It takes time for tissue to heal and settle down before the necessity for further surgery can be assessed. Any follow-up procedures which might be necessary could then be undertaken by Carlos or by Ian on subsequent visits. Looking at the project as a whole, the problems seemed almost insurmountable, but as Elvira said: 'If we want to do this, and we are willing to work towards it, then we'll do it! You'll see, Marjorie, we will meet again and work together in Lima!'

There are, of course, teams of doctors and nurses who undertake this type of work in the third world in areas other than Lima but, since Carlos was established in the city there were already in existence nursing and ancillary services. As the discussions progressed, Carlos and Ian realised that there might be problems regarding the complex anaesthesia necessary for their patients. It seemed unlikely that there would be, at that time, an anaesthetist skilled in this particular area in Lima. The help of an experienced anaesthetist was therefore essential. Since first undertaking the surgery of maxillo- and craniofacial deformity, Ian had been working with just such a man – Dr Duncan Ferguson. The wily pair thus conspired to infuse Duncan, who could truly be described as a 'canny Scot', with their own enthusiasm for the projected programme of surgery. The campaign planning had begun!

We did not realise it then but the discussion which took place in the Ambassador Restaurant in Blythswood Square, Glasgow, on that spring evening in 1974, gave rise to a great adventure which eventually was to lead us to David!

II
IS PLASTIC SURGERY
JUST A FACE-LIFT?

My native city of Glasgow features prominently in the story of plastic surgery. This title is somewhat misleading, since 'plastic' has no connection with modern synthetic substances but is derived from the Greek word 'plasma' meaning to mould or shape. Applied to David, the term is particularly accurate since his face has been moulded using skin, bone and tissue from other parts of the body.

Numerous methods have been used in David's reconstruction – some of them old and well-established – others more recent. Skin grafting is one of the older methods, and this was first developed in Glasgow. In the late nineteenth century, John Wolffe, a Glasgow eye-surgeon, transplanted portions of full-thickness skin to cover raw areas. These are still known as 'Wolffe grafts'. Later, in the first decade of this century, Sir Harold Gillies devised the tube pedicle. This was a flap of full-thickness skin which was rolled up into a sausage-like tube before being moved to another area. Both of these methods were used to treat the horrible injuries of the two world wars, and both were used in the reconstruction of David's face. The first bone graft ever carried out was in Glasgow Royal Infirmary. In 1870, Sir William MacEwen bone-grafted the arm of a young man. David, in his time, would undergo many bone grafts.

Around 1900 it was discovered that cartilage could also be used in nasal reconstruction. Ian used a lot of cartilage in the reconstruction of David's nose and jaw. Cartilage, however, presented one problem and that was that it tended to become twisted. In the late 1950s Thomas Gibson, a plastic surgeon, and Brian Davis, a bioengineer, both of Glasgow, solved the problem by showing that the twisting could be eliminated by cutting the cartilage in a certain way. Then in the late 1970s Ian developed a method of storing cartilage from cadavers which totally abolished the problem without resorting to special cuts.

In the mid 1970s my husband – the man who was to become not only David's surgeon but his father – working in Glasgow with his senior colleague, Ian McGregor, helped to illustrate that certain areas of skin and subcutaneous tissue have their own blood supply and could therefore be lifted up on the blood vessels and moved, without fear of losing the blood supply – without which the flap would die.

It was before this, in January 1968, that Ian and I, together with our three small daughters, went to live in Stockholm in Sweden. Ian had been awarded the Lock Travelling Scholarship of the Royal College of Physicians and Surgeons of Glasgow. He was to work at the Karolinska Hospital and study the surgery of cleft lip and palate. It was while we were there that he heard about the pioneering work of Dr Paul Tessier, of Paris, who had been developing new techniques in craniofacial surgery. In certain conditions of severe deformity, Tessier was moving the whole upper jaw, in others the orbits and the eyes. This was a gigantic step forward in the correction of face and skull deformity. The surgery was performed with the co-operation of neurosurgeons. It was the beginning of the team approach to this kind of problem.

Ian was greatly stimulated by all this and resolved that when he returned to Glasgow he would make every effort to set up a craniofacial team. He did indeed do this with the help and support of J. Scott Tough, the director of the Regional Plastic Surgery Unit at Canniesburn Hospital. At that time, the team consisted of Dr 'Rab' Hide, a neurosurgeon, and Dr Derek Henderson, an oral surgeon. This was the nucleus of the first craniofacial centre in Britain, and it was the only such team in the UK for many years. Large numbers of patients with facial deformity travelled from many parts of the world to be treated. In this way Ian and his colleagues were able to build up considerable experience and gain international repute. The programme also attracted many surgeons from other countries, including our friend Dr Carlos Navarro.

Microsurgery is another development which has further advanced reconstructive surgery. Under the microscope, vessels as small as 0.5 mm in diameter can be sewn together and blood flow re-established. Using the Glasgow blood supply concept, areas of skin can be raised and the blood vessels divided and joined to vessels in other areas. Thus the face can be reconstructed from the skin of the abdomen, back or chest. Muscle and bone can be transported in the same way, using microsurgical techniques; complex reconstructions can therefore be performed in a single stage. Microsurgical techniques have allowed the replantation of fingers and limbs to be carried out, thus obtaining the ultimate in rehabilitation – total reconstruction!

I hope that now, when you hear the words 'plastic surgery', you won't immediately think of cosmetic surgery – things like younger faces, nicer noses, bigger breasts and getting rid of baggy eyelids. This is part of plastic surgery, but by far the greater part of my husband's work is reconstructive. Plastic or reconstructive surgery today deals with congenital deformities involving the face, skull and hands; cancer of the skin and the head and neck area; treatment of acute trauma and post-traumatic deformity; acute hand injuries and rheumatoid arthritis. Surgery to remove a tumour frequently leaves a defect which has then to be corrected. If a breast has to be removed it is possible to have it reconstructed and if a tumour of the face has to be removed this area may have to be re-formed. The deformity of cleft lip and palate can be repaired so that the patient not only looks better but also speaks well. The plastic surgeon can also be a very effective 'trouble-shooter'. There are many times, for instance in orthopaedic or cardiac surgery, when, due to the nature of the surgery, defects of the limbs or chest cannot be closed directly; using grafts and flaps the plastic surgeon can reconstruct the raw area. For David, and thousands like him, plastic surgery is not just a face-lift.

III
PREPARING FOR LIMA

Carlos Navarro is Peruvian, but he was born in the United States of America in Kansas City, Missouri. After graduating from high school he entered one of the oldest universities in the continent of America, the Universidad Nacional Mayor de San Marcos in the 1950s. Unfortunately, due to student unrest between 1959–1961, it was closed down. Because of this Carlos left Lima and went to study in Miami where he obtained his MD degree. He completed his internship at Jackson Memorial Hospital, Miami, in 1966. From 1967 to 1970 he was a general surgical resident with the world-renowed cardiac surgeon, Michael De Bakey, in Baylor University Hospital, Houston, Texas. His three years of training in plastic surgery were also at Baylor with Dr S. Baron Hardy.

By the time Carlos finally went back to Lima in 1973 he was a very well-trained plastic surgeon. He encountered many frustrations during those first months after setting up practice. Both he and Elvira often wondered if, in coming back to their own country, they had given up too much, but fortunately for a great number of people there, they stayed. In Lima it was not possible for Carlos to obtain the type of equipment that he had been accustomed to having in the USA. This was due mainly to the unstable character of the country, both politically and economically. As is often the case when dealing with situations fraught with difficulty, many seemingly minor irritations – lack of operating gloves, dressings, needles, and suture material, for example – add up to a constant challenge from day to day.

When Carlos came to see Ian in 1974, part of their discussions centred around these 'minor problems'. It seemed to provide the stimulus of challenge rather than to worry them. They made light of the problems of adapting their methods to the equipment available. This may seem to be a cavalier attitude when they were dealing with real people and serious situations, but in fact it enables them to cope with their frustrations without dwelling too much on them and becoming bitter. Moments of extreme tension and strain are often best handled by a deliberate easing of the atmosphere with a joke or light remark. There is a fine line between being sensibly confident of one's ability to solve a problem using experience, skill, and technique, and falling into the trap of regarding oneself as all-powerful and invincible.

The more I learned about Charlie – during his years in the USA Carlos adopted this American-style abbreviation – the more I came to realise that he and Ian, although from very different countries and culture, are remarkably alike in many ways. Ian was a child of the Second World War when, in Great Britain, nothing was ever thrown away or wasted. In 1953 when he began his studies, something of this attitude remained in the hospital service. So in his clinical training Ian learned to be careful and economic in his use of all materials. Habits acquired like this are not easily forgotten. The disciplines we learn during the years of our studying and training usually stay with us for ever!

Although expanding rapidly, in 1975 craniofacial surgery was still relatively new. There existed only one or two centres in Europe and the United States capable of offering this specialised type of treatment. This being so, it would be unreasonable to expect a specialist team at that time in Lima. Therefore for Charlie to undertake the organisation and preparation for the visit of Ian and Duncan, the anaesthetist, to Lima was a mammoth undertaking.

Since there was no organised system of socialised medicine in Peru there was no way of financing expensive programmes such as those needed for craniofacial surgery. There was also no affiliation of hospitals and universities which usually initiates and stimulates teaching and research. It was not that Charlie had some crazy notion that he could instantly create a whole sophisticated training programme, but he was realistic enough to know that to succeed he needed the enthusiasm of his colleagues and the younger doctors. Above all, he had to have financial help.

Financing a programme of surgery for patients who, by and large, could offer no payment in return, was a major problem. There was no lack of patients but unfortunately most of them were poor and unable to travel to any of the established overseas centres for treatment. A social aid system had not yet been developed in Peru and so that potential avenue was closed. As Carlos's planning progressed, other patients heard that he was bringing a surgeon from Scotland to perform some surgery, and people came to his office to find out exactly what was happening. One field in which Ian was greatly experienced was that of rheumatoid hand surgery in which diseased

17

finger joints can be removed and replaced with silastic ones. Several patients came who were greatly in need of such treatment and were absolutely thrilled with the opportunity to gain pain-free and mobile fingers once again. Fortunately these people were wealthy and very happy to pay a substantial fee for this surgery. The fees were then used by Ian and Charlie to bring the poorer patients into the clinic. Shades of Robin Hood!

Meanwhile, back on the home front, Ian too was thinking of the proposed visit to Lima. He had had no difficulty in persuading Duncan Ferguson to join the project. He and Duncan had many lengthy discussions, and tried as best they could to make a realistic evaluation of what equipment they might need. Like squirrels we began to hoard everything we thought might be of use. Many drug firms constantly send out samples of drugs, dressings, bandages, needles, syringes, suture material and the like: we saved them all. Duncan corresponded with Charlie to find out what anaesthetic equipment was available so that he could take with him anything he felt would be essential. One strange piece of information came to Duncan from Charlie: curare, a drug which is used in modern anaesthesia to obtain muscle relaxation, was not available in Peru. Since the South American Indians had used curare in a crude form as a poison on the tips of their arrows for hundreds of years, this seemed incredible.

The nursing staff in the Plastic Surgery Unit in Canniesburn Hospital, and in the Nuffield McAlpin Clinic, where Ian also worked, gladly helped us with our project. Everyone gathered equipment which would otherwise have been thrown away; 'disposable' material was not disposed of, it was carefully cleaned and put into Mr Jackson's box for Peru. As the time of our departure came closer, cupboard-cleaning became a regular occupation in both hospitals, whether necessary or not, and anything unlikely to be used was simply added to the 'spoils'. The native of Glasgow is an enthusiast, whether it be for his whisky, football or, more importantly, good deeds like these. Another unexpected source of help, entirely outside the medical scene, was British Caledonian Airways. It had always been our custom to use this airline because we had been very satisfied with their service. We contacted them and briefly explained the purpose of our journey to Peru, and that the amount of medical equipment we wanted to take was proving a problem in both size and weight. We had hoped that they might be willing to charge a lower rate on the weight of the equipment so we were amazed and delighted when they said that for such a cause they would transport it free of charge. They asked for nothing in return – not even a suggestion that it would be nice if we would use their airline again. We were very appreciative of their help then and, as you will see, had still further cause for gratitude in the future.

The weeks and months seemed to pass very quickly and the planning and hoarding continued. A lot of sustained effort went into making Charlie's dream come true, but finally, in November 1976, we were ready to make our first trip to Peru.

IV
HARD WORK IN LIMA

The weeks of planning and preparation were now behind us, and it was with great excitement and some degree of apprehension that we began the first leg of our journey. The distance between Glasgow and Lima is approximately seven thousand air miles and we were routed through London and Caracas. Although Peru is a long way from Scotland, our association with Charlie and Elvira had forged a link between the two countries.

Peru covers an enormous area – it is roughly twice the size of the state of Texas and several European countries, including the United Kingdom, could easily fit within its borders. The population is not accurately known, but it is approximately seventeen and a half million. The white population makes up only about thirteen per cent of this figure. Fifty-four per cent is mestizo (a mixture of Indian and Spanish culture) and thirty-two per cent is pure Indian. Spanish is the official language but many different Indian languages exist, particularly in more remote areas.

Public schooling is free at primary and secondary levels. Urban areas usually have both primary and secondary schools but even primary schools become sparse the further away from the cities one goes. In spite of increased government aid for education in the past few years the incidence of total illiteracy is extremely high. Many people send their children to school only until they learn the most rudimentary skills. Children in urban areas are more often to be found in the markets helping their parents, or begging in the streets, selling flowers, newspapers or hand-made goods, than in school.

Catholicism, recognised as the religion of the majority, provides many educational facilities in the rural areas. The government has brought about some much-needed changes in health care in the past few years. There are probably around two hundred hospitals in Peru. In 1981 an Emergency Health Care Plan was instituted which included setting up a nutrition fund to help young and expectant mothers, and building health centres in rural areas and shanty towns. Immunisation against diphtheria, whooping cough, tetanus and polio is available, as is tuberculin testing, and vaccination against smallpox.

Plague, leprosy and malaria, however, are still a serious problem and an attempt is being made to combat the incidence of these diseases by de-ratting and the killing of insects. In the cities, bacteria such as the one which caused David's disease are carried by parasites on dogs, cats and vermin. A contributory social security scheme exists for employees and workers. Social insurance is compulsory and the benefits cover sickness, disability and old age. Unfortunately many people in the Indian community think of the hospital as a place one goes to die, and they tend to treat it as the antechamber to the cemetery. This attitude to hospitals will take a long time to change, particularly among rural Indians. Many of them still rely on, and trust in, the old ways. The 'curandero' or accepted medicine man moves around his own area, rather like our general practitioners, taking care of sick people. He uses herbs to make medicinal broths and also makes paint, pastes and ointments with them.

Like Glasgow, Lima is built around a river, but unlike Glasgow it almost never rains. The whole of Peru lies within the tropics, so the contrast with the chill, rain-soaked west of Scotland is enormous. Lima is large and sprawling; there are some beautiful residential areas but unfortunately the general impression is one of dirt and decay. Thousands of people live in conditions of extreme poverty and it is impossible to be unaware of this. In the slum areas there is frequently no form of sanitation, piles of waste material rot in the streets and children play among the filth. Yet, on the surface at least, the people do not seem to be unhappy or discontented. One often sees children playing happily in their own fantasy world, blissfully ignorant of their surroundings, even though rats may be scurrying about in the same street.

During our final approach into Lima on that first flight we wondered how we would fare going through immigration and customs. At that time, Peru was ruled by a military government and many situations were made more difficult because of this. Charlie had promised to meet the plane and would thus be on hand to help. Immigration posed no problems but we were not surprised when there was great consternation over our large box of medical equipment. With Charlie's help, we explained to the officials exactly what the box contained and the purpose of our visit to Peru. In spite of lengthy discussions, arguments and pleas, we were not allowed to take the container with us. It was not until the next day, when Charlie had conferred with the Ministry of Health, that our precious supplies were released.

As most international flights arrive in Lima very early in the day, it was still only mid-morning when we finished unpacking. Charlie took us down to his office in the Clínica San Felipe. Ian and Duncan inspected the facilities, checked over the list of patients to be seen and the schedule of lectures and discussions which had already been organised. In the two weeks ahead they hoped to pack in as much work as possible. Their working days were long and hard, beginning early in the morning. They relaxed a little over lunch and then resumed operating, finishing in the evening only when the surgical cases were completed – this was never before nine. They would then see relatives and consult with any patients who were still waiting hopefully. Time was never wasted. Whilst Duncan was busy either getting a patient ready for surgery, or taking care of a patient who had just had surgery, Ian and Charlie would be checking on the other patients, reassuring relatives, or seeing patients for consultation.

At first, when I saw the number of relatives and friends who came with the patients, I was very impressed with the amount of moral support given by the whole family, but I soon learned that there was much more to it than that. Charlie explained to me that if a patient required blood during surgery the relatives were solely responsible for providing it. There is no blood bank, as we know it, and no organised system of providing blood even in an emergency. The surgeon will give the relatives an estimate of how much blood might be required and it is their responsibility to get the donors to the hospital in time to have the blood typed and cross-matched. They must also persuade the donors to be present during surgery because there is not a lot of refrigerated space for storage of blood, even for a short time.

A further graphic illustration of this was shown some years later. On a working trip to Lima in 1983 we took our daughter Sarah, then sixteen years old, with us. She was excited at the prospect of seeing David's country and she longed to be able to help us in some way. As it happened, her presence was of great importance. During major craniofacial surgery on a fifteen-year-old girl, an urgent message for more blood came from the operating theatre. The mother of the girl was distraught because two of the donors she had organised had not arrived and there was no one else at that time she could get to give blood. Sarah, I remembered, has the type of blood which can be given to anyone. I sent a message into theatre asking Ian if it would be all right to get blood from Sarah. 'I don't care where you get it . . . just get it!' was his response. We dashed across the city and brought

Sarah back and before she knew it she was on a table with a needle in her arm, donating blood! It was a very thought-provoking experience for her. From the family of the girl she received a gift of a lovely long-haired toy Llama. I am ashamed to think of the number of times my good intentions of giving blood were never carried out, and reminded of how much we in the Western world take for granted.

Within the building in which Charlie has his office are several doctors' offices – gynaecology, ear, nose and throat, and gastro-enterology are all offered within. The doctor pays rent, has to supply and pay for his own secretarial help and to contribute towards the cost of nursing staff. He can use the facilities such as pharmacy, laboratory, operating theatres, and patients' rooms, but these all have to be paid for separately. Apart from the most major cases, the surgical patients in Charlie's care go home after surgery. This is to keep the expense of treatment to a minimum. The surgeon can choose to waive his own fee but if a patient has to stay in the clinic afterwards then all other expenses must be paid. During Ian's visits, when a patient needs to be kept in the clinic and it is obvious that they cannot afford to pay, Charlie uses the fees from the wealthier patients to cover the costs. Very often the kind of cases they are doing fare better at home because the patients are looked after very carefully by the family, who are usually fearful of something going wrong, and will cry for help if they are at all concerned. It is impossible to get properly trained plastic surgical nursing staff, and thus, due to poor education and lack of experience, danger signs in a patient are often not observed.

There were many stresses to endure during that first trip, and one of them was the curfew enforced by the government. No one was allowed to be out on the streets between the hours of midnight and five o'clock in the morning – not at all the ideal situation when there are sick patients to be looked after who may, at any time, need attention. Doctors were supposed to have immunity if they were on emergency call, but there were known cases of doctors who had been shot and killed, even though they were on call and flying the obligatory white flag on their car. Surgical schedules were always organised with the utmost care to ensure that they would be finished in time to allow everyone to get home before midnight.

One of the cases of facial reconstruction which Ian undertook was that of a rather well-known public figure in Lima. The gentleman was very grateful for the treatment he received, which gave him considerable relief. At this operation Ian and Charlie were assisted by 'Willie' de la Puente, president of the Plastic Surgery Society, and observed by some of the older Peruvian surgeons. An embarrassing occurrence was that the compressed air, which is used to run the air-drill for cutting bone, ran out, and Ian was informed that there was no more available in Lima. The 'demonstration' had then proceeded with hammer and chisel. It was unusual at that time not only for a foreign surgeon to be working in Lima, but to be undertaking surgery which was rather revolutionary. Even more unusual was that Ian and Duncan were carrying out these procedures free of charge – a novel concept in Peru!

The story of this operation was reported in the press, then the television news network became interested. They asked that the three men should go along to the studio to take part in a live interview. This was rather difficult to organise; however, a time was arranged and, after completing their day's surgery, the three of them dashed off to the studio to be interviewed before seeing the evening quota of patients. As usual, time was at a premium and when they arrived at the studio they were immediately whisked inside, along corridors, and into a room. Before they knew what was happening Ian was sitting in a large leather armchair under a barrage of bright lights, having questions fired at him in very rapid Spanish. Charlie and Duncan were meanwhile being seated to the side, and Charlie could hardly contain his laughter because he knew exactly what had happened. On seeing the three of them, the interviewer had immediately assumed that Ian, with his dark skin, dark hair and moustache, was the Peruvian and that Charlie was the Scottish surgeon!

I'm sure there are many parents like Ian and myself who wish from time to time that John Logie Baird, our fellow countryman, had never invented television! There must be few households where parents have never heard their children protest, 'I'm the only one who never gets to watch that programme!' There are times, however, when as a means of communication it is unrivalled. Seeing an item on the television news, rather than hearing it on the radio or reading it in the newspaper, seems to impinge more strongly on the consciousness of most people. Amazingly, such was the impact of the interview that evening in Lima. The following day there were many calls to the Clinic asking for more information, and the day after that several people just turned up. Difficult as it is to turn people away it was not possible to take on any more new patients at that time. One exception was made because the surgery could be done in one stage. This was a little Indian baby with a cleft palate whose very young parents brought him from a small town near the Chilean border. The palate was operated on in Charlie's office, and the waiting-room became the recovery room. The baby was fine and the parents were absolutely amazed. Their happiness was delightful to witness.

Charlie's receptionist was adamant that all other requests for consultations would have to wait for the next visit of the Scottish surgeon. One young woman, however, would not be turned away. Her name was Martine. She worked in an institution in Lima called 'Tierra de Los Hombres', a branch of the Swiss-based 'Terre des Hommes'. It is my impression that this organisation does as much, if not more, for the unfortunates of the third world as any other existing charitable institution. In Lima, Tierra de Los Hombres looks after children who, either because of the death of their parents, or because of severe illness in their family, are temporarily alone. Very often young people like Martine will go out to these branch institutions and work for a year. If they are all like Martine I have the greatest admiration for them because she is an extraordinary young woman.

The institution in Lima is run by Fernanda and her husband, Pépé. I will respect their wish for anonymity by using only their Christian names. They themselves have adopted one of the small boys who came to the institution after the death of his parents. The institution is situated in a fairly respectable residential area and looks just like any other house in the street. It is a large house; downstairs are the living, play, dining and kitchen areas. Upstairs are four or five bedrooms for the children and for the girls who work there. Fernanda's helpers have always seemed to me gentle and pleasant young people and it is obvious when watching them that they genuinely care for their tiny charges. Apart from the young people who come over from Switzerland, the girls I have seen there have all been young Peruvian Indians. The house is plain, with no 'mod cons', but it is clean and full of love. Fernanda and her husband are tireless in their efforts for the children in their care, and to see the faces of the children light up whenever Fernanda comes into the room, is really delightful. Their main aim is to look after the children until such time as they can go back to their own families. Frequently the children cannot see their relatives for long periods because of the distance involved. Although the house is run on a very tight budget, no one who comes there for help is ever turned away without at least some counselling. Fernanda gives them what she can, be it a little medicine for a cough or cold, some salve for a wound or burn, or sometimes just a sympathetic ear. She is clever, bright and efficient, but the warmth of her smile conveys to these people an indefinable quality of caring and compassion.

Working for, and with, such a woman as Fernanda, it is little wonder that Martine also has all those fine qualities of character. She is gentle and shy but, fortunately for David, there is within her a quiet determination which is totally unshakeable! From time to time her duties would include taking children to the children's hospital, Hospital del Niño, for treatment. It was on one such occasion that Martine found David. While waiting for the children from the institution, she played the age-old game of hide-and-seek with others in the ward. She came across a little boy in a room, all alone, sitting in an old-fashioned high-sided metal cot. Like everyone else who first looked on David in those days, Martine could not quite believe her own eyes. The child appeared to have no face, apart from his big serious brown eyes and a lower lip. The little boy regarded her steadfastly but made no attempt at all to communicate with her. Martine quickly hid her consternation and moved across the room close to the cot. Kneeling on the floor, she quietly and gently began to talk to the boy. For a while it seemed that she was not going to get any response, but then he began to show interest and, before she had to leave, he was standing in the cot trying to talk to her, using sign language and making primitive noises from the large hole in his face.

The picture of that small mutilated face remained in Martine's thoughts and on every subsequent visit to the hospital she looked for David. It upset her to find that on most of these occasions, David was alone. He was clean and he was fed, but in the busy day of the hospital ward there was no time to give him what he needed so very much– love and compassion. He merely existed from day to day. He was, for the most part, an object of pity and was often ridiculed by the other children in the ward who, with the thoughtless and ironic cruelty of the young, would call him 'Pinocchio'. Several weeks passed and Martine began to realise that the child was not having any treatment. The possibility of taking him to the institution occurred to her and she approached the surgeon in charge of David. She suggested that, if the child had no relatives – she had already ascertained that in all the months he had been in hospital he had never once had a visitor – and it was not possible to treat him, then would it not be preferable for him to be taken care of in the institution. There he would be with other children who were also alone and could perhaps begin to make some closer relationships with them and the people who would be taking care of him. The surgeon agreed to think about it. When Martine next came to the hospital he told her quite abruptly that he could not consider letting David go to the institution since he had made arrangements for him to go to the United States to have surgical treatment. Martine was elated – finally, this poor, lovable little infant was to have a chance!

For several weeks Martine did not see David but she thought of him constantly and wondered how he was faring in America. Imagine her horror when, one day, she returned to the hospital and found him alone, having had no treatment of any kind. She was both sad and angry. What could she do? Would it have been such a loss of face for the surgeon to have allowed the child the comfort of being looked after in a smaller institution, where he could have been given a lot of love and more time than the already overworked nursing staff in Hospital del Niño could afford? Could it have been that, lacking the experience or ability to treat the boy himself, this man was not going to allow anyone else to try? It is a sad comment on a man who has taken the Hippocratic oath.

Martine was confused by the whole situation, and it was in this frame of mind that she watched the television interview given by Charlie, Ian and Duncan. She listened carefully to what Ian was saying about facial deformity and the hopes they had of being able to help at least a few children during their stay in Lima. She already knew Charlie because he was the one to whom the children from the institution were taken whenever they needed plastic or reconstructive surgery. She decided that somehow she was going to take the little boy from the hospital to see the 'gringo' surgeon. 'Gringo' is a term used for a foreigner, especially of Anglo-American origin. For a long time it was a term used with scorn; nowadays it is a fairly commonly used word with no intended insult. Martine was determined that she was going to persuade this man to help David.

Martine never did volunteer too much information about how she got David from the hospital to the San Felipe Clinic, and we thought it prudent not to enquire. She brought David to the Clinic around ten or eleven in the morning. At that time Charlie and Ian were already in the operating theatre. The receptionist told her that there was no possibility of seeing the doctors that day as they had a full operating list, with many patients to see later, and that, in any case, there would be no more surgery on that visit. Martine caused no fuss. She quietly and efficiently found out where the surgery was taking place and that the surgeons would be returning to the office afterwards. Then, with

David by her side, she simply sat down to wait. In the hallway outside Charlie's office there was nothing on which to sit, so Martine and David sat on the steps leading to the next floor. When finally, at the end of a long and busy day, Ian and Charlie came back to the office to see the people who had been patiently waiting there, they were first met by Martine who asked that they examine David. One glance told them there was no possibility that evening of taking time for the detailed examination needed. They explained this, but gave Martine a promise that they would see her with David, the next morning.

The following morning I went with Elvira to the Clinic to help in any way I could; we knew that it was going to be an impossibly busy day. The hallway outside the office was very busy. Relatives of the little patients who had already been operated on had come to say 'thank you', and to say how happy they were with what had been done. It was moving to witness their happiness and to see how sincerely anxious they were to show us their appreciation. We were given small gifts to take back home to our own children and we were very touched by their thoughtfulness. Many of the gifts were made by themselves – little bead bracelets and necklaces, drawings done by their children, and other attractive articles.

On entering the office, the first person I saw was Martine. It would have been impossible not to notice her – she is so lovely – but I will never forget the first glimpse I had of the tiny little Indian boy sitting on the bench beside her swinging his legs. At first his face was incomprehensible until I realised that what I was seeing was a mop of beautiful black hair, two wonderful big brown eyes with a lollipop stick protruding from between them, held there up against his forehead with his lower lip. I could not imagine what possible help could be offered to correct such a deformity – but there was little time to dwell on that; there was so much work to be got through – dressings changed, sutures removed, patients to be seen and paperwork to be completed. It was not until much later that I was able to hear the story of David.

That evening Ian told me briefly the circumstances of Martine and David. He said that never at any time had he seen such a loss of soft tissue and bone as this child had suffered. He had advised the girl that the best course would be to try to send the child either to Mexico City or to one of the centres in the United States where he might be helped. Martine was adamant, however, that they had always taken their problems to Dr Navarro and therefore they would only feel totally happy working with someone he trusted. This gentle but determined young lady then faced Ian squarely and said, 'Will you help David?' It came as no surprise to me to learn that my husband's answer had been 'Yes'. To have said otherwise would have been to shirk his moral obligation as a doctor. Even as he told me about it he was assailed with all kinds of doubts about his decision. In spite of these, he knew within himself that there was no other course he could have taken. The situation was that *if* David could get permission to leave the country and *if* Tierra de Los Hombres could manage to send him to Glasgow, Ian would do all he could to effect some kind of reasonable reconstruction. He asked me whether I would be willing to help him organise things for David if he came and of course I said I would. Serious considerations such as the financing of such a project did cross our minds, but we came to the optimistic conclusion that eveything could be organised when we got back to Glasgow.

In the very early hours of the following morning we took our farewells of Charlie and Elvira and were soon winging our way back to Scotland, and our own children.

V
PREPARING FOR DAVID

The journey home was tiring but in spite of that, Ian and I spent some time discussing our stay and the commitment we had made to Martine about David. Even while we were in the plane, it all seemed a bit unreal. The possibility that the child would ever arrive in Glasgow seemed to be unlikely, but we decided that our first task would be to ascertain whether or not he could be treated within the National Health Service. There are countries whose governments have reciprocity as far as health care goes, but we did not think that Peru was one of them. Predictably, during our discussion of these financial matters, my beloved husband thought that I would be much better able to ferret out information of this kind than he would, so that particular job was allocated to me! In spite of Ian's outwardly light-hearted attitude, I knew that he was concerned that he would not be capable of the enormous task of reconstructing that sad little face.

Ian fell asleep but I continued to think. I could see quite clearly how it must have been when he saw David for examination. The surgeon part of him would have been absorbed and fascinated with the enormity of the defect – wondering whether it was a congenital anomaly, or whether it was caused by disease or trauma. Together with Charlie he would have speculated, probed, prodded – totally engrossed and stimulated – yet marvelling that one so small could have survived such a loss of tissue. Next would have come thoughts of how this extremely complex defect could be reconstructed. Reality was forced upon him by the calm and lovely girl standing beside the examination table who asked simply: 'Will you help him?' Could anyone have refused? I have never known my husband turn his back on a plea for help, and it would have been totally out of character for him to have done so then.

Back in Glasgow, financing David's visit became a priority. We were informed that it would be impossible for him to be treated within the structure of the National Health Service. Viewed unemotionally, this decision was not at all unreasonable. If permission were to be given to treat one person, then a precedent would be created and other requests could not be refused. That avenue being closed to us, I then approached two world-wide groups – 'Save the Children' and UNICEF. I thought that those large organisations would give us at the least some encouragement and might just possibly be able to assure us of help if the plans for David became reality. I wrote to each, not just once, but several times. From the former I received a letter telling me that 'they did not have money for that kind of thing'. From the latter I received no reply at all. I know that both of these bodies do some very fine work in their efforts to help needy children; therefore it is enormously disappointing to find that one does not get the courtesy of a reply from one source, or even good wishes to soften the blow of a refusal from the other. This was the beginning of a long entanglement with bureaucracy which was to remain with us for years to come.

By now we knew from our correspondence with Charlie that the problems in Lima seemed to be as insurmountable as the ones in Glasgow. Permission for David to leave the country required a document, signed by two surgeons, stating that it was impossible for the child to have the necessary surgery carried out in Peru. Unfortunately the surgeon in the Hospital del Niño, who was still officially responsible for David's medical management, refused to sign a document releasing David from his care. In order that David's chances would not be taken from him, Charlie and another of his colleagues gave written assurance to the authorities that treatment was available for the child outside of Peru. Ian and Duncan also submitted statements to the same effect and this was enough to secure a passport for David.

Towards the end of January I had explored many avenues with negative results. At that point Ian and I discussed the possibility of seeking help from the Church. Although we are members of the Church of Scotland and were sure that our local parish church would look favourably on our request, since the child would be coming from a Catholic country, we decided to approach the Roman Catholic Church first. Ian accordingly wrote a letter to Archbishop Thomas Winning explaining to him the circumstances of the little boy and the necessity of raising money to cover the expenses of his treatment. In his reply, Archbishop Winning expressed great interest in the case and said that without doubt the Catholic Church would be able to help David.

Although funding was uppermost in our minds, Ian and I had also discussed the problem of where David would stay if a prolonged period of reconstruction were to be undertaken. It was not until later that the immensity of this latter problem was appreciated by us. One morning in February, as Ian was leaving home for a long day in the operating theatre, a telegram arrived. 'Arriving tomorrow, love, Martine', it read. By that time for us, 'tomorrow' was today! Three months after our trip to Lima, David's arrival was now reality. Since Ian would not be home until very late that evening, I had no idea what I was going to do. There were times, there still are times, and I'm sure there always will be times, when I could quite cheerfully strangle my husband! That occasion was one of those. To my request for guidance as to what I should do, he looked at me with a kind of surprised expression on his face – always his first line of defence – and said: 'Oh I'm sure you'll manage, just go to the airport and do whatever you think is right!'

Before our children went off to school that morning I told them the news of David's arrival. They had heard of him, of course, because we had talked about him often, and they had also seen photographs. They were happy that they might get the chance to meet this little boy, and their main attitude seemed to be one of compassion for anyone who had to live with such an affliction. It was not their first introduction to facial deformity, they had seen photographs from time to time and had met other craniofacial patients. At one time we gave a home for several months to the wife and very young baby of a colleague of Ian's from Austria. The baby had a severe bilateral cleft lip and palate, and had been brought for Ian to operate on her. Because of this experience they had learned a good lesson: having a deformity does not necessarily make a person abnormal in any other way.

It was mid-morning when I received a telephone call from the south of England – it was from an Immigration officer at Gatwick Airport. He wished to ascertain that the child was in fact expected and was to have medical treatment. That officer, having quite correctly verified that David was entering the country legally, forgot then to stamp his passport – which caused us considerable trouble later. I arrived at Glasgow airport and watched, rather anxiously, the arrival of the British Caledonian flight bringing David and Martine to Glasgow. We later learned that the reason Martine couldn't give us more warning of their arrival was that, some weeks previously, Air France had promised to fly her and David to London free of charge. This depended on cancelled bookings and therefore there would be little or no notice when seats became available. Martine had also approached British Caledonian and they too promised that, if there were seats available, they would give them free passage from London to Glasgow.

The picture of David, that morning, as he walked up the ramp with Martine, is one that I know I will never forget. It is indelibly stamped on my memory. The sight made an impact on me which was almost explosive. I suddenly had that strange feeling of 'being outside looking in'. In seconds, our trip to Lima and all that had been accomplished there flashed back to me: the pictures I carried in my head of the poverty, and the sick children, all became instantly more real than they had seemed when we were actually there. I find it very difficult to describe my feelings; perhaps it was the stark contrast between David and his surroundings and my perception of the reaction of people in Glasgow airport when they saw David, which made me appreciate at that moment, as I had not before, and have not since, just how different he was! He looked strange – not simply because of the enormous defect in his face, but because he and Martine were dressed in a totally different way from anyone else. Martine looked stunning in a most beautiful poncho with a mixture of beige colours which complemented her skin-colouring and her lovely long blonde hair. David was a pathetically grotesque little figure. He was small, much smaller than I remembered from Lima. He was wearing old, scuffed, white leather boots, shapeless blue trousers, a russet-coloured jacket, a poncho, and a brightly-coloured hat, hand-knitted in typical Peruvian Indian style. The hat was pulled down so low over his forehead and round his cheeks that all you could see were his eyes and the awful hole in his face. My view of them was a moment of pure awareness which was startling in its clarity.

It would be very gratifying if I could say that this was the moment at which I decided that this child must immediately become part of our family. However, I didn't think that far ahead. If anything, I was more unsure than ever, and a little fearful of the responsibility being thrust upon me. I knew suddenly that I could not take Martine and her little charge to a guest house or hotel, there was nothing to do but take them home. Instinctively, I suppose, I wanted to protect this frightened little boy and make him feel safe.

We collected Martine's luggage, David had none, and set off. I had only one small spare room, containing a bed and a settee, which I could make ready for them. I put blankets and pillows on the settee for David and gave the bed to Martine. How confusing it must have been for David to have his surroundings suddenly look so different;

to feel so cold and not be able to understand what anyone – apart from Martine – was saying. I did not speak or understand any Spanish at that time. Martine was very tired and I encouraged her to lie down and try to sleep before the children came home from school. I knew that Ian would not return home early, and I thought that if we were going to be talking late into the evening she really should get some rest.

Martine did manage to sleep for a while that afternoon but David moved around the room constantly. I could hear him opening and closing drawers and occasionally when I passed by the door I could see him peeping out but, since he obviously did not want to be seen, I pretended that I had not noticed him! When the children came home I told them that Martine and David were upstairs. Linda was then fifteen, Susan twelve, Sarah ten and Andrew only seven. I reminded them that David must be feeling rather unsure of his situation and therefore they should not approach him until Martine was there to reassure him. About fifteen minutes later, however, Susan and Sarah came downstairs with David; he was between them, holding a hand of each. They had been talking together in their bedroom when he had come quietly into the room. I suppose they must somehow have expressed pleasure at seeing him and he accepted their friendly overtures and that was that! They immediately took him to see Linda and Andrew and from then on he was always with one of them, whenever they were not at school.

An event that took place that evening, which I know none of our children will ever forget, was their first meal with David. I had asked Martine if there was anything which he would be unable to eat. She said that she was sure he would try to eat anything I put on the table. I did not take her words literally, but I should have! I had prepared some chicken and, almost before you could blink, David had cleared his plate, leaving only the bones. Two of the children did not like chicken skin and meticulously cut if off and left it at the side of the plate; with lightning speed David picked it up and consumed it. The girls were amazed and absolutely speechless, but Andrew, being a bit younger, giggled. This was encouragement enough for David and thereafter his hand would dart out and grab any food within his reach. He tried to eat the butter from the dish, the sugar from the bowl, and drink the milk from the jug! Undoubtedly some of this behaviour was encouraged by Andrew's laughter but his obvious pleasure and satisfaction in acquiring the food was a little disquieting. He was like a little animal, determined to get the bits he wanted, and doing it in a way that did not invite contest. It was pathetic.

That was the first time in their lives that our children had ever seen anyone who obviously was not accustomed to getting enough to eat. Linda told me later she felt they were being paid back for all the times they had closed their ears to my well-worn lecture about 'all the starving children in the world . . .' in an attempt to make them eat their food properly! Two more things impressed us about David that night. First, was his method of eating. Considering his lack of palate, upper jaw, lip, and upper teeth, it was surprising that he could eat solid food at all. He placed the food in his mouth and with his tongue pressed it down and moved it around until it was able to be swallowed. To drink he simply held his head back and poured the liquid down his throat. The second was how meticulous he was when it came to clearing up any mess that he made during his meal. Apart from bones, nothing was left on his plate, and around his place at the table every crumb and drip was cleared up, either by eating it or cleaning it up with his napkin – another lesson for the Jackson children!

Since the following day would be a school day we tried to follow the normal routine, but even after Linda had gone to bed, David showed no sign of being tired. Getting him to sleep that evening was an exhausting business! He did not want to be washed, nor did he want to take off his clothes, and although I had at first thought that I could be of help to Martine, I finally left them alone hoping that she would do better without me. She eventually managed to take off his outer layer of clothing and put him in bed. During the few days that Martine was with us, I don't think his underclothes were ever removed – I think he was washed round about them! He would not stay in bed for more than five minutes. He got up, put his clothes back on and came downstairs again literally screaming his head off! If nothing else he certainly proved that he had a good pair of lungs. None of the children could sleep through all this commotion, so they got up to see what was going on. While they were around him he was fine, but as soon as they went back to bed and we tried to bed him, the crying began again. That night we tried every possible permutation. We thought perhaps if he was in a room with one of the children he would feel better, but he simply would not settle. We put up a camp-bed and tried it in each of the children's bedrooms, but as soon as he was left alone the crying began again and he tried to pull whichever of the children he was with out of bed. We finally accepted defeat. He must have been exhausted after all the hours he had been awake and travelling, but he would not give in to it. He fought off sleep and was playing happily on the floor with some of Andrew's toy cars when Ian came home, close to midnight!

Martine was a little worried and disappointed we had not yet managed to raise any money to pay for David's medical treatment. She knew that it would be impossible for him to stay and have his face reconstructed without funding. Ian told her about the recent letter from the Archbishop, and said that it was his intention to contact him again the following day. Unfortunately Martine could only be with us for a very short time as she had learned just before she left Lima that her mother was very seriously ill. She was needed back home in Switzerland. This was really a blow. I did not see how I could possibly manage on my own since I was unable to speak to David in his own language. By this time he had fallen asleep on the floor and Ian was able to lift him gently, carry him upstairs and lay him on the settee. We were very grateful when he did not waken again that night! Martine then told us, shyly, that it was now the day of her twenty-first birthday. We could not let an occasion like that pass without a little celebration so Ian opened a bottle of wine, proposed a toast to her and we wished her well.

The following day Ian spoke to Archbishop Winning. He expressed a sincere desire to help us with the problem of financing David's treatment, and felt that there might be many people who would be willing to give aid if they were aware of the problem. He suggested that it might be sensible to allow the local Catholic newspaper to print a brief account of David's arrival and his needs. Being an extremely busy man he was not able to have a meeting with us at that time, but said he would arrange for Father Tom Gibbons, who was then in charge of Catholic Child Welfare, to come to our home the following evening. Meeting and getting to know Father Gibbons was one of the unexpected bonuses of life. He was to be the liaison between the Archbishop and ourselves. Father Tom proved to be compassionate, understanding, thoughtful, kind, full of fun, and more important, to possess a great deal of common sense. I always felt better after a visit from, or a talk with, Father Tom. When I had times of doubt about what was best to do for David, or worries about his welfare, Father Tom was always able to help me put things in perspective and look at the situation objectively. From the first evening he came into our home, he was liked and respected by all of us.

Initially, that first evening, Father Tom had gone to the clinic where Ian was consulting. Ian had just finished his session when

Father Tom arrived and therefore it seemed more appropriate to come home and talk where Father Tom could meet David and Martine. As they were about to leave the Clinic a reporter and photographer from the *Evening Times* arrived and they also came to our home. We never found out how they had obtained their information about David, but it was clear that there was now no possibility of keeping his arrival secret.

VI
THE FIRST WEEKS

Even while still unsure of his situation with us, David always exhibited a great curiosity in all things new to him. That evening, when he first met the press, he was very interested in all the equipment belonging to the photographer. He was animated and excited, and he really seemed to enjoy the flashing of lights and posing for photographs. Although he did not understand one word of what was being said, he appreciated that the atmosphere was good and he was eager to please – at least for the time being!

There came a time not too many days later, however, when, on seeing yet another photographer coming into the house, he held up his hands to indicate – *No! No more cameras!* Ian and I were absolutely adamant that no photograph would be published showing the total extent of David's deformity. We felt that to have done so would have been to present him as a freak. After that first wave of publicity, although we kept people informed of David's progress by means of bulletins published in the newspapers, we allowed no photographs whatsoever – with the exception of one. It was not until two or three years later, when much of his face had been reconstructed, that we allowed his progress to be shown pictorially. The exception was made for Archbishop Winning. He believed there are times when it is necessary to shock people into understanding the suffering of others. Thus David had a photograph taken with the Archbishop in Canniesburn Hospital and it was published in a local Catholic newspaper. We believed Archbishop Winning's motives were right and this was certainly proved to be so. The effect of that pitiful little face staring out from the newspaper was devastating; there was an overwhelming response to the plea for help.

The results of the publicity were not without problems. Unfortunately we had spent only a little time with Martine before the newspaper reporters came on the scene. This, together with the fact that, under pressure, she found it very difficult to express herself clearly in English, made for quite considerable distortion of David's story. Martine explained that David's background was hazy. What was known about him existed only as a 'story' passed on by word of mouth. The account as Martine knew it was that David had been born in a remote area of the jungle. Apparently his parents had taken him to a local Mission seeking help for his condition. Every day it seemed that more tissue of the baby's face was being destroyed and in spite of treatment with herbal ointments and paint, the steady destruction could not be stopped. The reason for the condition was not known but when it became very obvious that the loss of tissue and bone was going to be much greater than his parents could have imagined, they asked the nuns to take their baby and look after him in the Mission. Unfortunately, these Missions do not have the facilities or staff to care for this type of case. So the baby was then, the story continued, abandoned by the parents, close to the Mission. Since he could not be cared for there, he was taken to Lima and put into the Hospital del Niño. It was there that Martine found him.

Martine told us that David was a Campa Indian. She said that although not a great deal was known about the Campas, they were generally considered to be peaceful, hard-working and caring people. She also said that one could only guess that the baby's parents had left him out of fear or ignorance of what was happening to his face. Perhaps they even thought that his condition was some kind of punishment from the gods. Martine told us that, far from neglecting their children when the adults were taking care of the daily tasks, very small children and babies are protected from animal attack by being placed in structures rather like wicker cages. Unfortunately this information was totally rehashed by the press and the story published was that David was imprisoned in a cage and starved. Thus David became 'Jungle Boy'.

Quite often, in bed, I would think about David's parents. I was never able to believe that they had abandoned him. I felt sure that when their attempts to get help for the baby were not successful the only option left to them was to leave him so close to the Mission that the nuns would have to take care of him. Had they not wanted him to live, it would have been a simple matter to have abandoned him where he could never be found.

Without the publicity that David's plight was given in the press, particularly the *Evening Times*, we might never have been able to help him at all. We are therefore very grateful to the fourth estate. Nevertheless, to be thrust into the public eye can bring many problems. It is very disquieting, and sometimes downright embarrassing, to have one's statements totally misquoted or rearranged so that the truth is destroyed and the sense distorted.

Manufacturing facts is even worse! On the occasion of the first 'birthday' David had with us, one newspaper gave an account of the party we supposedly had and of how David had blown out the candles on the birthday cake, and even some remarks he had made! The truth was that we had a very quiet family gathering and, although we did have a birthday cake with candles, without a mouth it was not possible for David to blow them out. At that time also his speech was still pretty unintelligible and to have quoted him would have been impossible. Our children learned then why we had frequently told them, 'You must not believe everything you read in the newspapers!' Fortunately that was just a piece of trivia which did no one any harm. To give credit where it is due, however, most of my dealings at that time were with a young man, David Steele, who was a reporter for the *Evening Times*. His genuine compassion for David was obvious and his reports were always presented with integrity. He never misrepresented us or sensationalised events, and for this I will always have respect and admiration for him. In more recent times I have been contacted on several occasions by David Hamilton, a journalist for one of the Sunday newspapers. He too has always given accurate reports of our conversations concerning David and has shown genuine interest in his progress and well-being.

It was sometimes very difficult, especially during the first weeks and months, to deal with the extra pressure of telephone calls and visits from journalists. David's story was extremely topical and each one wanted to be first with some new fact. As individuals the journalists were reasonable people, but they were being pressured by their superiors, and I, in turn, was being pressured by them. What could I tell them that they did not already know? I was feeling my way in a situation that was totally alien to me; I was often very unsure of what was right and wrong, or where the situation was leading us. I did not know if David would be allowed to stay in the country long enough to have surgery, or if he would remain with us. It wasn't that I didn't *want* to answer all those questions – it was simply that I couldn't. Although for me this was just one more frustration which could be very tiring, there was no lasting unpleasantness.

For Ian, however, things were very different. It seems that in all walks of life, when you have someone who through honest hard work has gained some measure of success, there are always others who would wish in some way to diminish him. It was thus for Ian. It was said that he had bought David to Scotland for his own gain, and hoped through the publicity to further his career. It is unfortunate that those people could not be with us when, on the many occasions both before and during times of David's major surgery, we felt very keenly the burden of doubt about our decision. Worry over David caused us many sleepless hours, but the love and support of our family and children helped us to remain steadfastly determined to help David, who was so alone. I am proud that my husband, in spite of the criticism and our own doubts and fears, was unwavering in his efforts to do whatever he could to help David. What we have gained from having David could never be bought, in terms of money, power or success.

When Martine left us to rejoin her family in Switzerland, she had been with us little more than a week. I was happy that Martine would soon be at home with her mother but was scared to death of the responsibility of looking after little David, whose language I could neither speak nor understand, and who could neither understand nor speak mine. Martine was very calm and told me again and again that she knew everything would be all right and whatever decisions we made for David would be the right ones for him. I was the one filled with panic and uncertainty! Martine gently explained to David that she was going away on the aeroplane and that he was going to stay with me and go back home in the car. She asked him to be a good boy, and she told him that she loved him very much. I was so nervous of what was going to happen when Martine walked away from us that I could hardly speak to say goodbye. I was sure that David would try to follow her and be so upset that I would not be able to comfort him. In fact as I, heart in mouth, watched her walk away, David moved round in front of me and very solemnly put up his hands to be lifted. I picked him up and took him home.

While Martine had been with me I had been able to note down a few key phrases in Spanish. We tried to cover all the basic needs such as eating, going to bed, going to the bathroom, washing, and words that would let David know he was a good little boy and we loved him. David has always had a really sharp sense of humour and a most marvellous giggle which can erupt into an uproarious, highly-infectious laugh. This laugh would usually greet our attempts at speaking Spanish. Even without the aid of the Spanish phrases, communicating with David for his basic needs was not really difficult. Children are all pretty good at indicating when they are hungry or thirsty, when they want to play, or when they are tired. Most of them leave you in no doubt when they are angry! One of the concerns my own children had initially was that they would be unable to tell how David was feeling, since he could have no expression on his face. They reckoned without his eyes. David has wonderfully expressive eyes and this was quickly appreciated by Andrew. 'It's easy to know what he is thinking, Mum,' said Andrew, 'you just have to look at his eyes!'

That evening, without Martine, my attempts at persuading David to take off all his clothes to be bathed were totally unsuccessful. I could not explain to him that I was not going to hurt him, that it really would be fun in the bath, and that he would feel so good to be clean and warm. I was despairing of what to do next when I suddenly had the idea that perhaps, if he could see how much fun it was, we could persuade him. Poor Andrew was selected for the demonstration and he did not think much of my idea. I pulled out all the bath toys that he had finished playing with some years before. That was enough for Andrew – he proved that he could be just as obstinate as David and let it be known that this self-respecting seven-year-old was not about to get into the bath and play with toys. Eventually we bribed him with the promise of some kind of 'treat' if only he would do it. David became so interested in Andrew splashing around in the bath that I was able to take off his clothes. When Ian lifted him up and put him in the water you would have thought his feet had been placed in boiling oil. He absolutely roared! We gritted out teeth and waited; after a moment or two he realised that nothing awful was happening and he stopped howling and carefully sat down in the water. His apprehension did not disappear immediately but it was not long before we could see he was beginning to enjoy playing with Andrew. There was never again any difficulty in getting David into a bath and eventually he became so fearless that he would 'swim', putting his face right under the water – I was the one who was scared then.

The bathing, however, turned out to be the easy part of that evening. During Martine's stay, David would lie down in bed only if she was in the room. Knowing that ahead of him lay many weeks of being in hospital, I had to develop a routine which would eventually provide some feeling of security. I put him in his bed, tucked him in, and kissed him goodnight. Then, leaving the room lit by a little night-light, I left him alone. It was no great surprise to see him standing in the living-room fifteen minutes later. Once again I tried all possible permutations – in Linda's room, in Susan and Sarah's room, and in Andrew's room – all totally without success. Finally I resorted to the only way in which I had ever been able to comfort my own children when they were frightened or sick; I sat on his bed and, stroking his head gently, I sang to him until he fell asleep. I did this night after night, with sometimes only an hour between each spell of comforting him. If I had made up a bed for him in our bedroom he would probably have settled down, but then he would have had to adjust again to being alone at night in hospital. Many mothers have gone through similar situations with their children, but it is so different being responsible for a child other than your own – suddenly you seem to lose confidence.

Although our children were very obviously happy to help David and showed a great deal of concern for him, those first weeks were not without family problems. It was easier for the girls, being older, than it was for Andrew. David had, from the beginning, related much more easily to the girls; I suppose he could sense their motherly attitude to him. Andrew was just as excited as his sisters at David's arrival and wanted to do things for him but he was smaller and tended to get pushed to one side. Until then Andrew had been the youngest in the house, and the only boy, and had been spoiled to some extent by his sisters. Now, suddenly, someone else became the focus of all their attention. The girls were able to discuss the situation in a more adult way so Andrew understandably felt left out of things. Unfortunately David, at that point, was being treated as someone very special by everyone and was thoroughly enjoying it. It was hard for Andrew not to be resentful when he saw how much attention I had to give to David. I realised this and understood his hurt and fortunately he tended to direct his frustration and resentment at me rather than at David. Luckily it wasn't long before David became more and more interested in Andrew's activities and wanted to be with him and play with him; then everything fell into a more normal day-to-day pattern.

As each day passed we were observing and learning more about David and more about ourselves too. We realised that too often our values and priorities were wrong. Watching a small boy's courage in the face of insecurity and fear made me very conscious of all the past occasions when I might have helped someone in need and didn't do so. We were learning to be humble. David's presence heightened our own awareness of all we had and took for granted – the love of family and friends, a home, food, employment and security. As we watched David being hurt by thoughtless behaviour and unkind attitudes we came to realise how much more importance is placed on how a person looks than on the kind of person he is. We watched the efforts of

David to build a new world for himself. He had to make himself understood and he had to understand us. We discovered that to have his own territory was of vital importance to him. Everything we gave him was hidden very carefully under his bed and no one was allowed to see or touch these things. He had a conglomeration of toys, books, pieces of unfinished biscuit, pieces of string – just anything that he had been allowed to keep. These, I am sure, represented a sense of belonging rather than a sense of possession. It was as if having those 'things', and a place in which to put them, made him part of the household and part of the family. Much later I recovered articles that had 'disappeared' – an oven glove, a gadget for slicing hard-boiled eggs, a wooden spoon and other things. Since he was unable to work all this out logically, I suppose what it did was to give him a basic sense of security and permanence.

Our children seemed to have already taken it for granted that David would stay with us, but for Ian and me it was a many-faceted problem for which there was no easy solution. It was difficult to know the right decision to make. Every day that David stayed with me made it more difficult to think of putting him into an institution; he, in turn, became more and more secure within our family. Because of this, Ian was plagued by a feeling that perhaps his professional judgement might not be so acute if he became too emotionally involved with David. He said that it was not uncommon for the friends or relatives of surgeons to be treated less thoroughly than other patients, in the hope of causing less trauma to the person. A departure from routine can often result in less adequate treatment than when the emotions are not involved.

One of the receptionists working at the Nuffield McAlpin Clinic at that time was Dorothy Marlborough. Dorothy was married and had three children. As she was often in contact with Ian she knew about David and about our dilemma of how best to look after him. She and her husband told us that they had all agreed that they would be happy to take David and give him a home. The Marlborough family truly opened their hearts to David. They met him in our home and then on several occasions David went to their home. They encountered one seemingly unsurmountable problem – David's fear of dogs. I had experienced this right from the very beginning. Martine had told me she had no idea why David had this overpowering fear of animals, but for him to be near them was terrifying. Even to see them through the window, although I might be holding him in my arms, caused him great distress. He would cling to me very tightly and indicate that he wanted to move away from the window. The Marlboroughs had a dog and found that if David became aware that the animal was anywhere in the vicinity, even behind a closed door, he wanted to leave. We hoped that in time David would become less afraid, but there were no signs then of this happening.

I was at this time under considerable strain. I was still running the household, working for Ian in his practice, and taking care of David. I hoped that somehow, when a definite course had been decided for David, I would know it was best for him, but I was very unsure of what that decision should be. Our own children were unanimously and totally against David going to another family. They were pleased that the other children wanted to help David but said we were being unfair and selfish to give him up. They argued that since we were responsible for bringing him to Glasgow we should shoulder the continuing responsibility. We took time to discuss the situation with them. We explained that giving him to caring people who were not directly involved with his surgery was a logical and rational decision. Ian told them that the most important factor of all was that David should receive the best treatment he was capable of giving him. He wasn't sure that if David became one of the family he could remain detached and professional enough to do this. Our thoughts went round in circles. How clear and uncluttered was the thought process of our children! To them it was simple. David had found a home. With love and security he was learning to trust us. How ludicrous to take that away just to give him the opportunity of what might be only a minimal improvement in his appearance. We are proud of our children for their attitude to David, but their emotional entanglement complicated our decision-making.

What of me? What were my thoughts and feelings at this time. I was confused and unsure. What was right, what was good, what was best . . . I simply didn't know. My feelings got in the way of concise, logical thinking. I was involved with this child on a much deeper emotional level than I wanted to admit – especially to myself. If I did, then I would have to face the fact that he had already become part of my life, my family; if logic and reason dictated that I should give him up – could I? I didn't know. I wasn't ready yet to answer that question.

Meanwhile the response to the Archbishop's appeal was so tremendous that Ian and I requested that all money be sent to a fund which would be managed by his office. We did not want there to be any speculation as to what we were doing with the funds. Many people did continue to send money directly to us and I think I was successful in replying personally to all of them, explaining that I would pass on their donations to the official fund. There were a few occasions when people sent money and requested that it be used in a specific way; then of course I complied with their wishes and informed them accordingly. The *Evening Times* also provided facilities for accepting donations and added them to the official fund. Many other newspapers throughout Britain took up the story and donations began to come in from all over the United Kingdom. Articles about David appeared in the press in Europe and even in the USA. A response came from all over the globe, but the greater part of David's fund was raised by the people of Glasgow and the west of Scotland. The knowledge that it would now be possible to arrange the beginning of David's treatment without any financial restrictions was an enormous load off our minds!

Because David's age was not known accurately, Ian thought that it would be a good idea to have the Anatomy Department of Glasgow University study X-rays of his bones to see whether they could give us some idea of how old he was. I believe that it is normally possible for them to do this to within a few months, but since in David's case the bones were scarred and the growth pattern distorted by the effects of malnutrition, his age could only be placed between three and six years. This was helpful, but the information on his passport was that he was then seven years old. Of course there had been considerable problems in getting this document, and since no one knew any definite details I suppose dates were decided upon in an arbitrary way. In addition to being seven years old, David was supposed to be three feet, two inches tall. Somehow he must have shrunk, since his actual height was at least three to four inches smaller than that!

In addition, David was having other tests carried out in the Plastic Surgery Department at Canniesburn Hospital prior to getting started on his programme of reconstruction. I felt very sorry that I could not explain why we were doing all these things. He was obviously apprehensive whenever we came to the hospital, especially so when he thought that someone was going to stick a needle into him!

During those first few weeks I was given tremendous support by my own family. My younger sister, Pat, gave me clothes which I had originally passed on from Andrew for her little boy Philip. Philip is about two-and-a-half years, and his sister Jane only a few days older than David. Jane and Philip became very close to David and they, like our own children, were hurt if people were unkind to David.

They were also concerned for his suffering after surgery. There were many times during the years of reconstruction when David did not look at all good, and to see Jane hug and kiss him, and tell him that he looked so much better already, was really quite moving. Major surgery inside the nose or mouth is usually associated with a very bad smell which is unavoidable. This is a very upsetting and embarrassing situation and many adult patients have told me that they find it difficult to come to terms with. Philip and Jane were never put off either by the smell or by the sometimes grotesque flaps and tubes of skin attached to David's face. They cuddled him and played with him at all times as though there was absolutely nothing amiss. Their love for David is simple and straightforward and they feel intuitively the importance of communication through touch. How much more it means when someone puts an arm around your shoulders, or gives you a hug, or simply takes your hand. The love communicated through a touch often needs no words to explain it. Why are we so reluctant to touch? Are we afraid of wrong interpretation, being thought weak or silly, or afraid of over-committing ourselves? In the case of illness, are we afraid of catching the disease? When a child is hurt, a mother will hug him and make everything better with a kiss. The pain is not magically taken away but the warmth and love of the mother's touch consoles much more than words ever could.

My brothers and their families were also of great moral support and always ready to help in any way. My task in coping with all my normal commitments, however, would have been ten times greater without 'Granny' and 'Aunt May', my mother and sister. Even after her day's work my sister was always ready to give up time for us. Whenever Ian and I had to go out she would make herself available to stay with the children.

All of my life my mother was a source of strength for me. She was a woman of tremendous strength of character. She was compassionate, but her sympathy was given in a constructive rather than in a pitying way. Married when she was just a young girl, in the early nineteen-hundreds, she had a long, full and hard life. She sustained me many times in my life with the wisdom she had acquired in her own. Her death in 1982 brought me great sadness but I am proud that a woman such as she was my mother. When Ian and I were struggling to decide on the best course for David, she advised us not to be pushed by outside opinion into making a hasty decision. Given time, perhaps circumstances would indicate more clearly what might be best. She was right!

Eventually Ian decided that it was necessary to begin David's programme of reconstruction. He wanted to start with minor surgery so that David's introduction to hospital in a strange country should be as easy as possible. We felt very badly about putting him through all the trauma involved when he trusted us. It was at this point that two of the important individuals in David's story came into our lives. Mary and Robert Rodriguez.

VII
A WAY OF LIFE

Mary's spontaneous and generous offer to help with David was of tremendous significance to us: to David it was of unparalleled importance. David came into Ian's life as a patient. Initially my role was to investigate the possibilities open to him as a foreign patient in Britain. After having seen David it would have been impossible not to help him in every way, but Ian and I had certainly not planned any closer involvement.

David's tests were all completed and Ian was ready to begin his surgery. With each day that passed, however, David's life was falling into a more normal pattern, and we were loth to catapult him into the harshness of separation again. Then Mary telephoned. I can remember her call very clearly. She told me that she had learned of David through the newspapers, that she spoke Spanish and would be willing to come along and explain to David why he was with us and what Ian was trying to do. Mary is extremely talented; she is a graduate of Glasgow University with an honours degree in languages and has experience of teaching handicapped children. Her husband Robert is Spanish, and he told us that Mary speaks his language so well that frequently people in Spain think he is the foreigner and Mary the native.

I was delighted to receive Mary's call just at that time, and gave her a brief outline of what had taken place so far. We arranged that she would come to see us that evening. Mary expressed some concern about her reaction on seeing David, since she had not previously encountered deformity of this magnitude. I felt sure that there would be no problem and that someone who was motivated so unselfishly by such a genuine concern would not reject David when she met him. Mary came on several evenings to get acquainted with David and her response to him was just as I thought it would be. His obvious enjoyment of being able to understand everything once again was good to see – Mary soon forgot about his deformity.

With David's surgery only two days away, the time had come to explain what was going to happen. From discussions with Martine, we knew that David had seen his face in a mirror, and had reacted with severe distress. What a shock it must have been! Although he was left alone a great deal he had seen other children in the hospital and was probably not expecting his face to look so different from theirs. How do you say to a small boy: 'Do you know you face isn't normal?' Mary began by asking him if he remembered making the long journey by aeroplane with Martine. From their first meeting Mary was very good at understanding what David was trying to say. He was able to tell her that he did remember the journey. She asked if he remembered the hospital in Lima, and although we could see that he did, he very obviously did not want to talk about it. Mary then asked him if he understood he had been there because he had been very sick and, because of this, his face was not quite the same as other people's. Again he indicated that he understood. Mary then asked him if he knew what job Ian did. In his reply she was able to make out the word 'médico'. When she told him that Ian was going to try to make a new nose for him, David literally erupted! He threw himself at Ian and hugged him. He danced, he shouted, he laughed, and he cried. David's tears were not the only ones in evidence at that moment. The sight of this trusting, happy little boy was a most moving one. When we told our children about it later that evening, there were four pairs of eyes bright with tears! Mary explained to David that he would be in hospital many times before he could have a nose, and that he would have a lot of discomfort. Nothing, however, could have dampened his spirits just then. The only thing that mattered was that he was going to get a nose!

Taking David to hospital to undergo surgery is not easy, and the passing of time has not made it better for any of us, including David. If anything, he is now more nervous. This is probably because he knows so well what to expect. It is the prelude to surgery that he fears and dreads rather than the aftermath, and he has an uncontrollable fear of injections. On that first occasion in Canniesburn Hospital he was very frightened and, although he was so little, he resisted strongly when the nurse tried to give him his injection for premedication. It was a relief when he began to quieten down and get sleepy. Ian carried out only a very minor procedure that morning so that he could gauge David's physical and emotional reaction to surgery. He also wanted to examine his face and the defect under anaesthesia. With David asleep it was easier to assess the soft tissue and bony deficiency accurately, together with the availability of local tissue for reconstruction. Until this time, Ian had considered the possibility that the defect was either congenital or caused by injury from an animal attack. Under examination, however, it was clear that David's defect was due to neither of these, but might be the result of noma, a disease which destroys bone and tissue and is caused by malnutrition.

As soon as David was back in his room after surgery I returned to the hospital. He was still sleepy but indicated that he wanted a drink. We couldn't allow him to drink so soon after surgery, of course, but he didn't want to understand that and became very frustrated and angry. Even now, when he knows and understands very well that he cannot drink immediately he wakens from surgery, he fusses quite a bit. He was fully awake by the time I had to leave him, and the look in his eyes when he watched me walking away is a look I still remember. I had pantomimed a little story to him, to explain that I had to go home to the other children for a while but that I would come back later. I am sure he understood and he certainly recognised the names of our children, but a look of absolute resignation came into his eyes. I hugged him and told him 'hasta luego', – which means 'until later' – but he lay very quietly, without moving, and his gaze never wavered as I left the room. As I drove away I felt very badly about leaving him behind, so obviously thinking that once again he had been abandoned. When I went back later that evening, however, it was very encouraging to see how his eyes lit up when I walked into his room. Although I could see in his eyes a look of almost disbelief, perhaps it was at that moment he really began to trust me.

Since the surgery David had undergone was fairly minor we had expected to bring him home very soon afterwards. The following morning, however, he did not seem to be at all well, and as the day wore on Ian became more unhappy about his condition. He did not appear to have any noticeable respiratory problems after anaesthesia, and there was no evidence of infection of the surgical incision, yet he was running a fairly high temperature. The following day Ian arranged for David to be seen by a paediatrician. He too agreed that David was definitely not progressing satisfactorily. He had a very mild respiratory infection, a slightly raised temperature, a slight degree of anaemia and some evidence of malnutrition. There was nothing to indicate any serious problem, nevertheless he was listless and unresponsive.

After five or six days, while his symptoms were no worse, his general malaise was more pronounced, and he did not seem to be responding to treatment with antibiotics. I thought that he looked as though he was beginning to lose weight quite rapidly, and Helen Baird, the nurse in charge of the children's ward, agreed. Helen is a great nurse and she had a good team of nurses around her: we were fortunate she was at Canniesburn during the years of David's surgery. Helen spent as much time as she could trying to coax David to eat, but nothing seemed to interest him at all. I spent a great deal of time with him every day and Mary came many times also. She talked to him and tried to persuade him to eat so that he would get better and be able to leave the hospital. It was all to no avail. At this point Ian and I both thought, since there were no signs of improvement, that it would be better to take him home. We hoped that having some of his own things around him would make him feel more secure while the company of the children might dispel some of his listlessness.

David's first admission to hospital taught Ian an invaluable lesson. On the third evening after surgery when David was so obviously unwell, Ian came to the hospital with me to visit him. This was not a professional assessment, but a family visit. Ian was completely unable to deal with the situation objectively and even began to have doubts about whether or not David might survive. He has never visited David again in that role and sees him in hospital only as 'his doctor'.

When David returned home, Granny became indispensable. She sat with him, sang to him, coloured pictures for him, coaxed him to eat, and gradually, with gentle but firm persuasion, she pulled him out of his lethargy. By this time it was almost Easter and she suggested that we go away for a few days with all the children. We had a very tiny cottage on Loch Long, and we thought that maybe Granny was right, fresh sea air would be good for David. Needless to say the girls and Andrew were delighted; it was not often that Ian was able to take time for a holiday. The drive there was lovely and David seemed to have perked up. We went to bed early that night and all of us were looking forward to the next day but it did not turn out as we had expected. The first two days were disastrous! No matter what we set out to do, David didn't want to do it. Whatever we planned to eat, he didn't want to eat it. In those two days his main activity was crying – oh, how he cried! The noise he could make was really unbelievable. Andrew was sure that because David's mouth extended into such a large hole, he could make twice as much sound! He nearly drove us crazy. We tried so hard to think of things to do that would make him happy, but the poor pathetic little boy could not, or would not, be happy. We didn't know what to do to console him, nothing at all seemed to please him and we also had the language problem to contend with.

Suddenly on day three he changed; it was as though a magic wand had been waved, and we never looked back from then on. He began to eat and to play and to enjoy all the many things we could do there. His favourite place to be was on the seashore wearing his 'wellies', where he could throw stones into the water. The transformation in him was amazing. Looking back on it now, I think that in the beginning he simply missed Granny! Perhaps the sudden change in his environment also upset him. Not understanding that we had simply taken him there to allow him to enjoy himself and get well, he may have been afraid of what this new situation meant. Eventually 'The Wee House', as he and our other children refer to it, became David's favourite place to go.

We will probably never understand the effect of that first hospital stay and the length of time it took for David to recover. After his short holiday, however, his general health was vastly improved and he continued to thrive. We have never had, at any other time, even after his most major surgery, the type of problems we had on that occasion. Looking back, Ian believes now that his condition was due simply to a general debility caused by his basic malnourished state when he arrived in Glasgow. He was, after all, a very small boy who had travelled a long, long way, who had left his own country and, in a few hours, arrived in a totally different one. He had exchanged the warmth of the sun for a bitterly cold wind accompanied by rain. Added to these upsets was the time change. Although the results of all his tests proved to be within normal ranges, except for the level of iron in his blood, and he appeared to be reasonably well, it is difficult to estimate what effect these abrupt changes create, especially in a small child who is by no means one hundred per cent fit. We tend to forget how very fortunate we are in the Western world where, because of the high level of health care, children need never be undernourished. To be on the safe side, however, Ian waited for several weeks after David's first surgery before he attempted any more. When we were sure that he was really fit and healthy we made arrangements to begin again.

By this time, apart from the ties that had developed between our children, the rest of the family and David, I had grown to love this child very much. It was going to be very difficult to give him up, but I refused to acknowledge this even to myself. My feelings were in turmoil. I was deeply involved with David, I loved him – how could I not – but what was the right decision for his future? I was angry, but didn't know why or with whom. Was I angry because chance had left this child with such a burden to bear? Was I angry because circumstances had thrust this responsibility on me? Was it the silent judgement of my children, who couldn't understand why, if I loved David, I found it so difficult to make my decision and say *David is mine: he stays here*? It was easy for them, I thought, they have their own lives ahead, they will leave, and all the worry, the work, and the responsibility will be mine. My anger was a little of all these things, but mostly it was directed at myself. That anger was mingled with a slight sadness. I was looking at me, I didn't like what I saw. I continued to struggle and reason with those seemingly incompatible feelings of shame and guilt and love.

The passage of time helped to sort out my confused feelings, as I came to understand that I worried too much about what other people thought or might think. Other people didn't really matter. If I knew within my heart that whatever was decided was for David's long-term good, then I could be strong enough to accept the pain of giving him up, and be happy about it. I learned too, despite my doubts and fears, that I could let the love I have for David guide me to make the right decision. If it was possible to keep him, I knew that this love, and the love and support of my husband, children and family, would be my strength.

The most important factor at that time was that David should have the best treatment possible; it was therefore necessary that Ian should make decisions as free from emotional pressures as possible. To have this freedom from pressures when making a decision is ideal, but we rarely achieve the ideal. In reality we have to concentrate on the hub of a situation and compromise a little in order to make a decision and follow it up in a positive fashion. We sat down together to look at the problem from all angles.

We knew that David's future should be planned to be as stable as possible within the boundaries drawn by his surgical programme. In the weeks David had been with us he had created bonds: he was clearly growing secure within our family. He was beginning to develop into quite a little character; he was happy and outgoing. To thrust him into a totally new situation at that critical time might mean an insurmountable setback for him. We felt that this would be morally wrong. If we decided to keep David with us, however, what would it mean? The opinion of our children was quite clear and I had accepted that I was irrevocably involved with this child. On the surface, therefore, acknowledging him as a member of the family did not seem to present any difficulties. Ian was also emotionally involved, his problem being whether or not it would be possible for him to remain objective about David as a patient. To give David the best possible chance of doing well both physically and psychologically, we had to provide a fixed point in his life. We knew the magnitude of the surgery ahead and we now knew that to leave him in hospital for long periods would be harmful to his trust and feeling of security. I was happy to learn to look after him and nurse him at home as soon as he could safely leave hospital after surgery. I could be reasonably confident because, since we lived very near to Canniesburn Hospital, Ian would be close at hand if I needed him. Without Ian's constant guidance I could not have managed. No other family would have such help available, thus David would have had to spend long periods in hospital and only brief spells at home. He would have no permanency in any aspect of his life; this would last not for months but for several years. If he moved into a 'non-plastic-surgery' family he would have to spend most of his life in hospital and this would present a problem in arranging education for him. It was after taking all those factors into consideration that we decided to keep David.

Since that decision we have many times wondered if it was the correct one for him, or for us. Given the special aspects of his case, I think it was probably the best course to take. People have often asked me if I think we have done a good job of bringing him up so far, and I find that very hard to answer. We have done the best we can; we love him as we love our own children and we teach him the same rules and principles we taught them. The problems facing parents today are more or less as they have always been. They are dictated by changing pressures of society on its youth, and so it is important for parents to be open-minded about these changes in order to help our youngsters live a good and productive life. Bringing up a handicapped child is different in some areas, but we had still to learn about that. Our immediate objective in 1977 was to get David settled into a normal everyday routine. In the future we would have to learn how to help him live as normal a life as possible, adjusting and changing as necessary around the timetable of his surgery.

There were so many things to consider and take care of; the problem of David's legal status in Britain being one of them. I had to make regular petitions to the Home Office in order to have continued permission for David to live in the country. Details of his surgical programme had to be given as well as proof of funding for his treatment. Apart from the sheer physical nuisance of repeating this every four to six weeks, there was always an underlying fear that at any time we would be told that David could stay no longer. Until the end of 1984 the position did not change. I still had to petition the Immigration Office at regular intervals – initially every month, recently every three months – in order to have his visa renewed.

Gradually we established a new routine. We had to plan the surgery; we also had to plan David's education. We did not know his exact age and I never believed at any time he was as old as indicated by his passport, the only document we possessed. We had to come to a kind of compromise between his 'official' age and the Anatomy Department's assessment. Mary and Robert were fast becoming members of our family and Mary was always willing to help us. By looking at picture-books with him and telling him the English equivalent for any object he knew in Spanish, Mary gradually introduced English words to David. He was becoming a really bright, lively little boy and he looked forward each day to the children coming home from school. He never seemed to tire of them. They, however, did sometimes tire of him! Like any small brother he could be troublesome. He did all the usual things – like messing up jigsaw puzzles and pulling apart Lego – but most of all he loved to sneak up to Linda's room. Being the eldest, Linda was having to fight for all the things that girls of her age love to do – wear make-up, use nice perfume and so on. Linda was not at all pleased to find that little fingers had been poking around in her eye-shadow and her lipstick and using her perfume. David takes great delight in giving 'frights'! He used to creep quietly up to Linda's room when she was studying and would suddenly be behind her chair tickling her neck. Scared out of her wits, she of course would yell and shout, and many a time I heard her say, 'Go away, David, you are really a wee pest!' As far as possible I tended not to interfere; I felt it was important for David to be treated normally by his new brothers and sisters. There are always occasions, however, when one has to act as referee. My own children accuse me of always favouring David, but I tell them that it is just because he is the youngest. Very often when he comes home from school the little rascal plays his 'giving a fright' trick on me, and when it works, as it usually does, he says delightedly, 'Got you, Mum!'

Little by little David was chiselling out his own niche in the family. He no longer showed any fear of being rejected, but he was still obviously trying very hard to do things that would please us. Because he was the only one at home during the day, he became my constant companion, and he was happy helping me around the house. Like any other small child, he imitated the actions and sounds of adults. To make the correct sounds was very difficult for him, and I remember one occasion when he and I both became sore from laughing at one of his attempts to imitate me. I learned then that a sound I made frequently was achieved by closing the teeth and very rapidly moving the tongue up and down in tiny movements; this produces a funny little 'ditditditditditing' noise! I remember as a little girl I used to be enthralled by my mother's superb skill in this field. Well, as David and I walked into Susan and Sarah's bedroom that morning he must have been just as appalled by the mess on the floor as I was; he picked up a piece of clothing, and shaking his head, imitated my sound! He couldn't do it the way I did, but nothing daunted, he curled up his tongue and made a funny little clicking noise way back in his throat. I'm not sure he ever really understood why I was laughing so hard, but he joined in anyway.

Now that David was fit and strong it was absolutely necessary to begin his schedule of surgery without further delay. Again, he was frightened and reacted very strongly against the injection of pre-anaesthetic medication, and to the actual induction of anaesthesia. This was upsetting for David and for me and especially for Ian. It was very difficult for Ian to be objective when he could hear David, so terrified and crying, in the anaesthetic room. Once the operation had begun, however, he became immersed in the technicalities of the surgery and there were no problems. We adopted a slightly unusual course for David's pre-operative routine thereafter. Whenever it was possible, David was put first on 'the list'. Ian would give him his pre-medication injection at home, around five-thirty or six o'clock in the morning. It still was not easy, because even away from the hospital David was always terrified of the needle and fought against it. After that I took him on my lap and comforted him by cuddling him and singing to him until he fell asleep. On these mornings my girls were just great. They got up quietly when I told them, and helped each other and Andrew to have breakfast and get ready for school, because I couldn't leave David alone. They made the back seat of the car ready for him with pillows and a blanket, then they came in quietly to kiss him goodbye.

I know that to be able to organise things in this way was a 'perk' I could have only because Ian was both surgeon and father, but I don't think anyone, knowing what David went through in all those years of surgery, would grudge him this small privilege. I am deeply grateful to all the hospital staff who gave me moral support on those mornings. Everyone involved worked to make it as easy as possible for me to leave David and feel confident that all would be well. Our good friend Duncan Ferguson was David's anaesthetist and he became 'Uncle Duncan' to David. Duncan organised the pre-medication injection which we gave David at home, and was there when I carried him into the anaesthetic room. He helped to quieten and calm David when he began to cry. If Duncan was not available, his position was usually taken by Dr Douglas Arthur, who is also a friend. As the parent of a handicapped child, I learned to appreciate more than I would ever have believed possible, the confidence and strength these doctors could impart by their calm efficiency.

Mary, Robert and I were able to be with David in the evening when they brought him from the recovery room into the intensive care ward. Poor Robert found it very hard to see David in the pain and discomfort that is inevitable after surgery of this kind. Robert has a very soft heart – we thought at one point we might have to get a bed into David's room for him. David is, and always has been, very stoical after surgery. Beforehand Ian always explains exactly what he is going to do, so when David wakes up he will not be afraid and upset by the various painful and peculiar procedures that have been carried out on his body. At that time Mary would listen to Ian and then relay all this information to David. She explained things several times to be sure he understood, but it must have seemed very peculiar to David that he had to have surgery on his abdomen in order to get a nose. He was a very bewildered little boy. This surgery was the first of many major procedures for David. On the first evening he came home, Granny sat with him. She looked at the small figure asleep in the bed and said, 'He's such a little boy to face so much – the wee boy David.' To her, David's will to fight, his courage and endurance as he faced the battle to have his face reconstructed, was akin to the courage and endurance that David the shepherd boy displayed against Goliath.

While David was recuperating from this operation we continued to discuss the best method of beginning his education. The constant changing of David's situation – sometimes at home, sometimes in the hospital, periods of surgery, periods of post-surgery, and quiet periods in between – would not easily lend itself to the opportunities available to us. He could not be sent to the local school since he did not speak or understand English very well and he had had no formal education of any kind previously. There was a centre in Glasgow where non-English-speaking children were taught English when they came into the country initially. Unlike David, however, these children arrived secure within a family situation and although they have a similar language problem they fortunately do not have the problem of severe facial deformity. For David there would be many times during the course of surgery when the reconstruction would inhibit his movements and he would not be able to look after himself. The teacher in Canniesburn unfortunately did not speak Spanish and so could only teach David at a play level; further, because he would be in and out of hospital frequently, a steady contact could not be maintained. Yet education was vitally important, so we began to explore all other possibilities.

As I mentioned, family and friends rallied around us when David came. Among them were Edward Miller and his wife Margaret, who have been friends since our schooldays. When visiting us they met David and were impressed by his liveliness. They already knew how he had arrived in our family. When Eddie heard of our perplexity over the matter of David's education, he said, 'Surely I could be of help to you in this matter!' We would never have asked Eddie to use his position as Director of Education for the Strathclyde Region to help us, but given freely in friendship his spontaneous offer was very gratefully and happily accepted by us.

Under Eddie's guidance, the Education Committee reached the best possible decision. David was to have a tutor at home and, when well enough, in the hospital. Mary Rodriguez, an experienced teacher, and already his friend, was appointed. She submitted a curriculum of the work she hoped to cover which was accepted by the committee; it was decided also that she should send a progress report to Mr Miller from time to time. Mary was absolutely meticulous about this. She kept a careful note of all her teaching time with David, and on occasions when, because of surgery, she could not work with him, she recorded these missed hours and made them up at other times. Thus my dining-room became a classroom. Robert and Mary created a marvellous collection of 'flashcards' which Mary used to teach David the alphabet. These and the brightly coloured pictures which David made were pinned up all round the walls of the room and always provided a topic of conversation at dinner parties!

We established a very carefully adhered to routine. David had his 'playtime' when he scampered up to his bedroom with his juice and biscuit, leaving Mary and me to have our coffee in the kitchen. I think he was afraid that if he stayed with us the classroom routine might just go on! At lunchtime Mary went home and then returned to begin

59

afternoon lessons. Mary's task of teaching David was certainly not without problems. She very quickly realised that his time in hospital in Lima as an infant had taken a very serious toll as far as his general development was concerned. For instance, when a normal four- or five-year-old begins school, it is taken for granted that he or she has a firm grasp of the routine in the home and within the family. When these children are being taught to read from the usual first-stage teaching books, they are at least familiar with the terms used in the books. Phrases like 'Here is mother' had no meaning for David whatsoever, because he did not even know what a 'mother' was! David had missed all those wonderful times mothers spend with their small babies, talking, singing, playing and gradually bringing them to an awareness of the world around them and their place in it. We tried as best we could to make up for all the things he had missed and he was a fast learner!

The speed with which David was learning English was amazing. As his vocabulary grew he would occasionally mimic a word one of the children had used, and this usually caused great merriment! He loved to clown around (he still does) and it was as though the children's laughter signified his acceptance. It was exciting for Jane, Philip and our children to get ready for David's first Christmas with us. He was very definitely taking in and storing things away in his head for future use. On Christmas Eve we had a birthday cake, complete with candles, for Ian's birthday, but David suddenly became quite agitated when it came to present-giving time. He didn't want to hand over his present, and we finally realised that he was trying to tell us that he wanted this 'thing', this 'event', for himself – not just the present, but the whole birthday. He had experienced several family birthdays by that time and he was making it quite clear that enough was enough, and now it was his turn! It was then that, at the suggestion of the children, we decided to make his birthday in February since that was the month in which he had arrived in Glasgow.

Although for David many good things were happening, there were also many not so good things. There was surgery, which he accepted because he never lost sight of the final goal – to get a nose. There was school with Mary, and like any other child he sometimes liked it, and he sometimes did not. Adjusting to the world around him was not very easy. In the hospital in Lima he was in contact with only a few children and the nursing staff. Now he was constantly meeting people and being stared at. I never at any time tried to hide David. I took him with me when I went out shopping, or visiting friends, just as I had done with my own children. I am sure we have all been guilty of staring at facially-deformed people – it is almost an involuntary act. We usually then turn away quickly so as to cause as little embarrassment as possible to the unfortunate person with the defect. To continue to stare, draw other people's attention or make detrimental comments which can be heard, is absolutely unforgivable. Happily, most people are concerned and caring; if they caused David any upset, it was because they did not understand how to deal with the situation. It is not easy but I have always found it better, as does David, when people show they are shocked then immediately cancel it by being direct, and asking in a straightforward, concerned manner, what had been the cause of the problem. Many people encouraged David by telling him they realised how much he must have suffered and how brave he must be. The words one uses are not as important as the tone of voice and manner in which they are delivered. Even when he did not understand English, David knew very well when someone was being friendly and kind.

If, as a parent, you are confronted with the situation where your own child sees a child like David, and says, 'Oh Mummy, look at that boy, he looks like an animal!' or something equally awful, you shouldn't hurry them away saying 'Shush, don't look!' In the past I have done that, thinking that it was kinder to the child to remove my own young offender. I know now, however, that the child feels safer and less an object of scorn if the other mother quietly and briefly explains to her own offspring that he or she is very lucky not to have had all the pain and suffering that the other has obviously endured. Most people are not intentionally unkind and I think the remainder are simply unthinking rather than deliberately hurtful. There are nevertheless two incidents which will always remain in my mind. Both happened, at separate times, when I was with David in our local grocery store. Once a very well-dressed middle-aged lady turned to me and quite deliberately and callously stated that she felt that I did not have the right to impose David's appearance on the general public, and especially not in a food store! On another occasion, a lady, also of an age to have known much better, addressed herself directly to David and told him that with a face as horrific as his he should stay indoors until Hallowe'en! I made no direct reply in either case but simply bent down and quietly told David that we would pay no attention, such unkind, nasty remarks were not worth getting upset over. To make a scene would make things even more unbearable for David.

After David had been with us just over a year, his behaviour began to fall into much more normal patterns. No longer did he watch for a chance to do something which he knew would please; instead, like any other small child, he would sometimes behave in a way which he knew very well would *not* please. Just how secure he was beginning to feel was brought home to me one evening when I was sitting at the kitchen table with all the children, while they were eating their dinner. Linda asked for a second helping, and after she had been served David said: 'More please, Mum.' Andrew, who was still a little jealous of his place in my affections, said – not unkindly – 'You shouldn't say "Mum", David, you should say "Marjorie".' David looked at him solemnly and said very slowly and deliberately: 'Linda say Mum, Susan say Mum, Sarah say Mum, you say Mum – and I say Mum.' I just did not dare to laugh and neither did any of the children, because the way in which David spoke simply did not brook argument. From then on he never again called me 'Marjorie', he always said 'Mum'. Strangely enough it took him much longer to refer to Ian as 'Dad'.

David's own security in the family, however, forced us to think about the future. Nothing had been settled. We realised suddenly that it was unthinkable that he should go back to Lima. What would be his future there? Where would he go? Who would be responsible for him?

We had learned from Charlie and Elvira that for David to go back to Lima would be tantamount to a living death. It would be highly unlikely that he, an Indian, would be fostered by a white Peruvian family. In Peruvian society the level of the Indian population is usually that of the servant class. The Navarros deplore that this is so, but it is an irrefutable fact. David however is not only Indian, he is deformed; because of this he would not be employed by any faction of society. He could not lodge forever in the Hospital del Niño, nor even in the institution of Tierra de Los Hombres – not because they would be unheeding of his plight but because they have neither the facilities nor the finances to keep him all his life. He would be given as much help as possible, but as a twelve- or thirteen-year-old he would have to move out and become responsible for his own survival. How? Two avenues only would be open to him – begging, or making money by displaying himself as a freak.

Robert, Mary, Ian and I went round and round in circles discussing the best possible way in which we could help David. Into their minds as well as ours came the plan that seemed to offer a possible permanent solution to the problem – adoption. It was of the utmost importance that David's status be made legal and permanent – and this seemed to be the way to do it. Robert and Mary told us that they would be willing to adopt David. They, like us, would never have willingly allowed David to be sent back to Peru, and were prepared to wait until we were ready to make a decision. Our children were once again totally opposed. They loved and respected Mary and Robert, who were really almost like family by this time, but they remained firm in their belief that David should continue to be part of our family.

Ian and I decided that it would be in David's long-term interest if Mary and Robert could adopt him. The Rodriguez are much younger than we are and, since they have no children of their own, could perhaps give David much more attention and help than we could. Also, at that time, our own children were unaware of the fact that Ian might leave Scotland to work in the United States. He had already entered into discussions with the Mayo Clinic in Rochester, Minnesota. It would have been very wrong to ignore the serious effects a decision to leave Scotland might have for David. We knew that the winters in Minnesota are long with very low temperatures. The effect that the cold might have on David's reconstruction worried Ian a great deal. He did not know how the tissue would react, and it would be unthinkable to lose all that had already been accomplished. Robert and Mary also were not sure that they would remain in Glasgow much longer. If they went back to southern Spain, then David would be living in a climate ideal for his reconstructed face and the Spanish culture would also be closer to his own.

My inward struggle with conflicting emotions continued. Once again I fought to hide the distress I felt at the thought of losing David. I tried very hard not to let my judgement be swayed by these feelings.

David meanwhile was coping very well with the surgery and with its effects. As can be seen from the photographs there were times when he looked very strange indeed. His attitude to all those changes, most of which in the first years only seemed to make him look worse, was very positive. There were many times when he and I laughed together about what 'Dad had done this time!' – for his spontaneous calling of Ian 'Dad' did come. It was Ian's habit to 'peep' the horn as he drove into the garage in the evening. One evening when David, who was running around in his pyjamas, dressing-gown and slippers, heard him arriving he ran to the door shouting, 'Dad's home!' On this occasion Andrew knew better than to protest!

Although David's treatment was progressing well I was a little worried about his social development. As long as he was with me things were not too bad, but there were times when he might be with the children and then people were more unkind – especially other children. This was very hard for David, but it also created great difficulties for Linda, Susan, Sarah and Andrew. All of them got into some heated arguments over poor David! It was probably hardest for Andrew because he was so young. Often at school other boys would tease him about David, asking 'Where's your monster today?' Because of all this, I thought that David should be exposed gradually to situations where he was with other children of his own age, not always protected by me, or his brother and sisters. Jane already attended the playgroup at our local parish church, and Pat and I thought David might be helped to cope socially if he joined. Alice McPherson, the playgroup leader, was terrific. She is a very bright and compassionate young woman who understood David's needs immediately. In spite of a little opposition to David being brought into the group, Alice was able to persuade the majority that it would be morally wrong not to give him the opportunity afforded to any normal child.

When David was not in hospital he attended the playgroup two mornings a week. Mary made up this loss in his school work by adding a little to his afternoon session. He quickly grew to love going to playgroup. For increasingly longer periods of time he would forget how he looked and gradually the other children did also. Alice usually had two or three mothers to help her each morning and they saw for themselves that, apart from his face, David was no different from their own children.

There were relatively few problems among the other children in the playgroup. One very small girl was afraid when she first saw him, but Alice dealt with the situation so well that David was not aware of this. Some of the children kept their own distance for a while but they very soon accepted David's looks and he became simply one of the group. By talking with some of the mothers, Alice discovered that the other children seldom mentioned David at home. This indicated that his presence was not unduly upsetting. Small children can be a problem when they see David, because they are not at all inhibited about staring at him, especially at close range. I generally approach these little ones fairly quickly and explain that David was not as lucky as they, and did not get a nice nose, or mouth, and is having them made by the doctors instead. In the very early days of David's reconstruction, one tiny girl, on being given my usual explanation of David's looks, said, 'Well, the doctors have done it all wrong, they have made his face inside out!'

With the help of the playgroup David was really progressing on all fronts. His diction was amazingly good. Ian found this rather surprising because his palate had been constructed from soft tissue only and was at that time still rather thick. David had none of the usual nasality of the cleft-palate patient. His vocabulary in English was growing by leaps and bounds. One of the hardest aspects for me was to be consistently firm in the way in which I disciplined him. It would have been so easy to spoil him. He suffered so much; when he knew that surgery was approaching he became very afraid. After surgery, he had to contend with all the discomfort and get used to the changes in his appearance but he never used this as an excuse for avoiding tasks he didn't want to do or as a means for doing something which was normally forbidden. He was learning to be part of a family; he was learning to share and to enjoy giving gifts as well as receiving them. He no longer hid things under his bed to ensure complete possession. I had to spend a lot of time helping him to form words properly and enunciate them clearly. I had to be very strict about this, and he frequently became very frustrated, and had tantrums. I already had experience of this kind of behaviour pattern as I had gone through many months of speech therapy with Susan. At the time she was approximately the same age as David and her tantrums were just as fierce!

Granny and Aunt May were the ones who did the spoiling, just as they had with our other children. Granny spent many hours singing to David and teaching him all the well-known nursery rhymes. Just about that time, Paul McCartney's 'Mull of Kintyre' was very popular and David was able to give a fair rendering of this. We have very good friends who live in Ardrishaig, a lovely town situated on the shores of Loch Fyne, on the west coast of Scotland. Uncle Tom and Aunt Florence were greatly delighted to hear David singing this tribute to their native heath! David would often go to the park with Aunt May and Jane and Philip. Their favourite game was to be cowboys and rope Aunt May's two dogs like steers. Aunt May was 'pardner' and even now when David speaks to her on the telephone, he shouts 'Hello Pardner'.

By this time David had gone home many times with Mary. She and Robert put a lot of effort into helping him over his fear of dogs. They

65

have a lovely Old English Sheepdog called Sally and very patiently they taught David that he did not need to be afraid. It was really marvellous to see how much he enjoyed contact with animals after he had conquered the terrible fear he had had initially. David became part of Mary's family also. Grandma and Grandpa Sheridan spent a lot of time with him but a special favourite of David's was Mary's young sister, Claire.

All this time, Ian and I never ceased to worry about whether we had done the right thing for David. When he had to face life-threatening procedures we agonised over whether we should have brought him to Glasgow in the first place. Father Tom Gibbons often shared our discussions; he understood our doubts but said we should look at things more positively. He realised we loved David very much; further, he believed his coming to Glasgow had a purpose. David's plight had touched many hearts and homes; he made many of us examine our attitudes to people who are facially deformed. Sadly, many people equate facial deformity with mental retardation and this causes much unhappiness for the child and for the family. There is no better cure for resentment of one's own situation than to look at children like David, to watch them face disability with optimism and courage. One's own problems diminish beside theirs.

By the summer of 1979 two very important decisions had been made. Ian had finally decided that he would leave Scotland and make a new beginning at the Mayo Clinic. Robert and Mary had also decided that they too would leave Scotland and return to Spain. As a result Ian and I made the hardest decision of all – to let David go with Mary and Robert. We love and respect these two young people and we had no reservations about their ability to love and care for David; our unhappiness was purely selfish. We knew that David loved Robert and Mary and we truly hoped that he would come to look on them as parents. Children want to be the same as everyone else and I thought that when David settled into a normal routine he would make the transition and Mary would become 'Mum'. Mary, however, always maintained that no one could ever take my place as David's mother. In taking David, Mary and Robert were not only prepared to do their very best for him, they were leaving themselves open to a lot of heartache too. Mary assured me that, if we ever thought it best that David should come back to us permanently, they would support that decision. We know they do not think of themselves as being special, but they are two unique young people.

When we parted with David in December 1979, we knew that he would come and spend the following summer with us in Rochester. Ian planned to continue his surgery at this time. Loving David as I did, it was hard to let him go, but I did think that perhaps the separation would help Ian to regain an objective perspective on David's problems. No matter how much he wanted to keep his role of father separated from that of surgeon, his awareness of David's defect could not but be uppermost in his mind. I watched him playing with David and I could see him almost constantly assessing the last procedure and mentally criticising his own work. No matter how immersed he was in being 'Dad', the surgeon was always looking over his shoulder. There were times during the night when he would waken me to tell me that he had just thought of something that might work the next time. I could have done without those nocturnal discussions on facial reconstruction. There were nights, too, when I knew he was afraid that some of his decisions for David might not be right but when he left next morning it was with his usual determination to do his best.

Initially Ian had been accused by some of bringing David to Glasgow to glorify himself, or as a means of advertising. I found it unbelievable that anyone watching him work with David over the years could lack the humanity, never mind the perception, to realise that this was no self-glorifying action but simply a straightforward effort to carry out his job to the best of his ability and in so doing help another human being. Isn't that what the practice of medicine is all about? The fact that he became so emotionally attached to David did nothing to detract from the skill and effort he put into his work, but it did add to the strain on him. I knew the anguish he would feel if anything should happen to David – and there were two occasions in particular when we thought that David might not survive the surgical procedure. On the plus side, however, he got a tremendous amount of moral support from the registrars and from the nursing staff. One of his colleagues in particular, Khursheed Moos, contributed an immense amount of work, emotional input, and moral support to David's programme of surgery.

From a personal point of view, our leaving for the United States was a particularly dark time for me. Parting from my family and my own country were two of the hardest things I have ever done. I was able to do it because I believed in Ian and trusted his decision. We parted with David in the same way: we trusted Mary and Robert and we believed that for David, we were making the right choice.

VIII
NEW BEGINNINGS

By the end of January 1980 we realised just how right we had been not
to bring David with us to Minnesota. Since winter here sometimes
lasts from the beginning of November until the end of April, Ian's
fears concerning the reconstructed tissue of David's face may well
have been realised. At that time we had no way of knowing whether
the blood supply would be good enough to allow it to survive.

The first months of settling in a new country are very difficult and
while we had problems in Minnesota, Mary and Robert had theirs in
Spain. They had decided to settle in a small community in the south
which was ideal for David since the temperature very rarely drops
below 55 degrees. Robert was setting up his own business, something
which takes a great deal of energy, and Mary meanwhile was
investigating the possibilities available for David's education. Mary
and Robert had visited the area with David the previous summer. At
that time David had withstood several months of fairly intensive
reconstructive surgery and Ian thought that he needed a complete
break somewhere where he could enjoy the sun and sea air, to build
up his strength again. It was not possible for us to leave Scotland then
as the children were still in school. Mary and Robert were, as usual,
ready to help and the arrangements for David's much-needed holiday
were made.

He had a wonderful time and came back looking very fit. He even
seemed to be looking forward to the next procedure, for on the first
evening, when he was in his pyjamas ready for bed, he ran and took
out a handkerchief from Ian's drawer. Many times when Ian was
observing David as he played around the house he would, for lack of
anything else useful at hand, pull out his handkerchief and use it as a
measuring tape in order to make approximations of the length of the
tissue which might be available if he wanted to swing skin flaps
around from one position to another. David could always make a
comment which would reduce us to laughter, and on this occasion he
said to Ian, 'Here you are, Dad, you can measure me now – with a
clean handkerchief!'

Robert and Mary's decision to live in Spain was a marvellous solution to our worries about David in Minnesota. Another tremendous bonus was that they had already made friends there, so there were people who already knew and accepted David. One of the most difficult things for David, even now, is to have to integrate with a new group of people and endure the awful period of waiting for acceptance.

Mary investigated all the schools within the surrounding area and finally chose Swann School for David. This is a small school run by 'Miss Glenda', where the children are basically taught English, but have lessons in Spanish also. Many of the children were Spanish-speaking so there was an excellent opportunity for David to retain his skill in both languages. After becoming reasonably proficient in English he had become lazy in his use of Spanish. Like most children he wanted to be the same as the children he played with. Glenda had met David the previous year, so she realised that there might be problems with both pupils and parents when David was enrolled in the school. Her sensitive understanding of the situation made everything much easier for David. She explained to the other pupils before David arrived why he looked the way he did, therefore his appearance was not unexpected and his entry into the school was as smooth as possible. Children usually accept facts about handicaps if they are explained honestly and simply, and it does help the deformed child if his classmates know what to expect. It does not altogether eliminate the trauma for him but usually shortens the period before he is accepted.

Once David was established in school and Robert's business had got off the ground, he and Mary began the work of getting a legal adoption organised. To go into all the details of all the times we have petitioned lawyers, courts, embassies and consulates would make for very boring reading. Let it suffice to say that we have never let up in our efforts to secure an adoption. While still in Glasgow, Mary and Robert could only have been considered adoptive parents for David if he had lived with them for three months continuously. This rule is to allow the authorities to visit the child at any time to ascertain whether he is happy and whether the circumstances of the home are suitable for him. In David's case, however, it was not possible for him to be at home for that amount of time. Mary and Robert could not take responsibility for David in the days immediately after surgery and so there was no way in which they could qualify to enter the adoption programme.

In Spain they renewed their efforts, but after months of having their hopes raised only to have them dashed again, paying fees to lawyers and getting nothing in return, Robert, in desperation, wrote to King Carlos of Spain. Several weeks later he received a reply from the King saying that he thought David's case was worthy of special attention. He told Robert to expect to be contacted by someone from his legal office, but once again the weeks and months passed and nothing more was accomplished. We may touch the hearts of kings but it seems that they alone are powerless to help – not even one small Indian boy!

By this time it was becoming very clear that without a birth certificate no lawyer would undertake any proceedings towards adoption. Without an adoption certificate David would never have legal status in any country except Peru. Let me jump back a little in time and tell you about an incident which clearly indicated to us that we must not give up our endeavours to make sure David would have security in the future. In Janury 1978 Ian and I made another working visit to Lima – a trip which was made infinitely easier for us by British Caledonian who took care of our travel arrangements and once again carried our equipment free of charge. When David first heard of our trip he made it quite clear that he wanted to come with us. It was difficult for him to accept that I was leaving but I realised that as I had not left him since his arrival in Scotland it made him feel very insecure. I patiently explained several times that we were not taking Linda, Susan, Sarah or Andrew and that he would be safe at home with them and Granny and Aunt May. Finally, with Mary's help, I told him that we were going back to the hospital in Lima where he had been and that Dad was going to operate on other boys and girls who were sick. We have to presume that this triggered off some unpleasant memories for him, because from that time on he has never again asked to come to Peru with us. While we were gone he was happy to tick off the days on the calendar with Granny!

At this time too we received some unexpected but very welcome encouragement from Lady Catherine Bowes. She was then president of the Anglo-Peruvian Society which, at her instigation, donated some money to the fund for David. She contacted Ian personally and from him learned the facts, as we knew them, about David. In her role as president, she made the society more aware of the situation in Peru and what we were trying to do there, so that future monetary help would be used where it was most needed. It is so necessary to present the full facts both to the receivers and those who donate. Although no longer president, Lady Bowes is in touch with us regularly for news of David and is always ready to help us.

While we were in Lima on this occasion our fears of what would happen to David, if it became necessary for him to return, grew a thousandfold. Elvira and I tried very hard to find out more about David's background. We thought that there must be papers relating to his admission to the hospital in Lima and we hoped that they would give some details of his family. If we were successful, we just might be able to establish whether or not a birth certificate existed. All Robert and Mary's efforts had led us to believe that such a certificate would be essential. We were very well received by all the staff, but no one was able to give us any information which was absolute fact.

Following this, we decided to try to speak to one of the Sisters from the Franciscan convent in Lima. After many attempts we finally arranged an interview with a Sister who had worked at the Mission where David was left, but she was unable to help us.

It was a pleasure to visit Tierra de Los Hombres once again and observe how much good work they were doing for the children in their care, but they had no further information they could give us either, so at the end of that visit to Lima we were no further forward. We were, however, now even more determined to find a way to make David's future legally secure. If we needed anything to spur us on we had only to think of the alternatives – begging, or living as a freak.

David's life was settling into a new pattern. He spent his winters in Spain with Mary and Robert, then as soon as school finished at the end of May he came to Rochester and Ian began his surgery again. His first summer in Rochester was particularly difficult. Once again he was thrown into a completely foreign situation; he was also without the comfort of 'Uncle Duncan' and all the nurses he knew so well. For the first time ever, David himself wavered. When we were alone in his room at St Mary's Hospital, he said: 'Maybe I don't need any more surgery now, Mum.' These are the hard times. I wanted to pick up my poor, frightened little boy and take him home. Instead I comforted him and tried to make him see that when it is all over, he will be really happy he was brave enough to go through with it and, more importantly, he will be happy with the improvement. Ian tried to accomplish as much as he could, but the summer months are short and we did not want David to miss too much schooling. I would usually take him back to Mary and Robert by mid-September.

These journeys back were very upsetting because understandably David was emotionally and physically considerably below par after weeks of surgery and had all the associated traumas – fear, pain, discomfort, dealing with a new look, and becoming dependent on me. We spent such a great deal of time together, not only while he was in hospital, but at home also immediately after surgery. On the first occasion I took him all the way back to Spain. I slept in David's bedroom, and on the morning I was leaving I awoke to find him lying in his bed staring at me with tears running down his cheeks, but not making a sound. I took him on my lap and held him tightly and all he said was, 'I don't want you to go, Mum.' I felt an immense feeling of despair but I tried to make him understand that the partings we had to have were sad for all of us, but that they were because we wanted him to have the best possible chance. Mary and Robert missed him very much when he came to Rochester: we missed him terribly when he was in Spain. He tried very hard to be brave but he was after all just a little boy – how could he understand? I knew that once I had left he would soon settle down again, but it tore me apart to have to leave him. After that occasion Mary met me in London and we parted as quickly as possible.

These were very trying times for Mary and Robert also. They had to ease David back into routine again. Children are most vulnerable when they are sick so he was feeling a little sorry for himself. It was only natural that David got more than the usual amount of attention and some spoiling also during the weeks when he was enduring surgery. I was not the only one to spoil him, however; Andrew and the girls were overjoyed to have him back and they also wanted to help him get through his surgery as easily as possible. They spent many hours reading to him and playing with him. The summers in Rochester are usually very hot and often humid. When one's head and face are covered in bandages it is much too uncomfortable to be out-of-doors. Apart from the surgery and the pain and discomfort associated with it, he had also withstood two or three general anaesthesias. Thus by the end of summer, when it was time to take him back to Robert and Mary, David had had a lot of cosseting and was not feeling full of bounce and energy.

The swelling resulting from facial surgery has to subside before an improvement in appearance can be noticed. This meant that when I was taking David back to Spain he often looked worse than on the journey out. As a result of this he many times had to endure people staring at him quite openly. I remember two incidents particularly because the people in question made absolutely no attempt to disguise their morbid interest in David's appearance. We were held up for several hours at Gatwick airport because of a strike of air traffic controllers. This was on the first occasion that I was taking David back to Spain. I had bought him a colouring-book to help keep him occupied for a while. He was working away quite happily when I became aware of a young man who was persistently and obviously walking backwards and forwards right in front of us in order to be able to study David's face. At first I thought I must be mistaken, but after several minutes I realised that I was not. He was indeed, without regard for David or for me, studying every detail of David's face. As I have said before, it can often be much more embarrassing for the handicapped person if an ugly scene develops, and so, not wanting to create one, I tried to ignore the man. At the same time I tried to shield David a little from his stares. Just when it seemed that he had finally left us alone he suddenly reappeared, but this time he had his wife and two children with him; they were unashamedly there with the sole purpose of 'viewing' David. How very sad!

Shortly after this we were given vouchers which allowed us to eat in the restaurant. We were shown to a table and had only been seated for a few moments when a middle-aged gentleman and his wife were brought to join us. The gentleman sat down, smiling to David and me as he did so, but his wife looked at David and said, very clearly, to the airline steward who was seating everyone: 'It will be impossible for me to eat or drink anything if I have to sit looking at that awful face.' Even in my anger and misery for David, I could still feel sorry for her husband. He was exceedingly embarrassed and, probably, very ashamed also of his wife's behaviour. I told David that we should be sorry for someone who was as ugly inside as that lady. Experiences like these are very hurting but one should not ignore them simply because it is difficult to explain such behaviour to the child. I believe it is better if children can be helped to understand that there are unfortunately a few people who seem to be without compassion. During family discussions we often talk to David about behaviour like this. We try to help him realise that although a few people may be cruel, there are many others who appear to be uncaring, but who may, in fact, act out of embarrassment or an inability to express their sympathy.

David's life in Spain was a new experience for him. Going to school wasn't like being in the dining-room on a one-to-one teacher-pupil relationship – that situation is stressful for both pupil and teacher. Mary is an excellent teacher and her patience with David was almost saintly, but there were occasions when I could detect, from the noises coming from the dining-room, signs of frustration on the part of both of them. I am glad that Mary was the teacher and not I – I think I would have strangled him! In Spain he was now one of a crowd and because of his appearance and all the insecurities of integrating with new people, he kept a low profile for a while. The classes were of a reasonable size and this makes it easier for him. It was not too long before the other children realised that he functioned in the same way they did, it was only his appearance which was unusual. His athletic ability is something that always helps to break down barriers and as time passed he became an accepted member of the class. Slowly he began to emerge as a leader in some fields – mostly, I believe, in the areas of sports and mischief-making! He seemed to be popular with the other children and they became very interested in his surgical progress. When he returned to Spain after his first summer in Rochester, they carefully examined what had been done and expressed satisfaction with the improvement!

Out of school Mary and Robert spent a lot of time with David walking in the hills and on the beach and thus his interest in what was going on around him was continually being stimulated. He was naturally inquisitive and as a result of this, and their encouragement, he was constantly gaining in general knowledge. He improved his talent at football by playing often in the garden with Robert. He spent a lot of time also playing with Sally, the dog, and the several cats that Mary and Robert have. David is by nature a loving and kind little boy and they fostered these attributes in him but they did not do so at the expense of discipline. David could, and can be, wild and uproarious, but together Mary and Robert produced a well-mannered, lovable boy.

For personal reasons Robert decided that it was necessary for him to change his job, and they moved to another area close to Cadiz. Apart from all the other implications, it meant that once again Mary had to look very carefully for a suitable school. This is not so easy in an urban area. Finally, when she thought that she had found one David resumed his lessons. Like the school in Marbella, lessons were taught in English, but in every other aspect it was unfortunately not at all like the Swann School.

As time passed, Mary noticed that all did not seem to be well with David and she discovered that his treatment at school was far from good. The teachers seemed to have little interest in whether or not he was happy and were only concerned that the younger children should not have to look at his face! One of his real social problems is that his features become more distorted when he is chewing and swallowing. Apparently he was made to eat his lunch facing the wall so that none of the other children would have to see him eating. It is incredible to find such a lack of compassion in a teacher! Instead of helping the other children to understand, they penalised David cruelly for something for which he was not responsible in any case. Mary also found out that he was being ridiculed in the playground and was sometimes locked in the bathrooms. On another occasion some older children painted him purple and from then on referred to him as 'the monster'. Mary was asked to take him away from school fifteen minutes earlier than the regular closing time so that the younger children need not see him at all. Robert was often away from home so Mary was mostly having to bear the brunt of all this by herself. David told Mary that he hated everything – them, the house, and the school. He said that he was going to run away. Very shortly after this it was time for him to come to Rochester again and we saw for ourselves the change this unhappy time had made in him. Gradually, over the summer weeks, he told us little bits about what had gone on at school. Meanwhile Mary and I were having long, expensive telephone calls discussing the situation and trying to work out something which would be better for David. Although the progress of surgery was promising, Ian thought that it might still be extremely hazardous to expose the reconstructed tissue to sub-zero temperatures.

Mary's solution was one which meant a great deal of sacrifice on her part. She told 'Miss Glenda' of the trauma David had suffered at his new school. Miss Glenda suggested that perhaps he might be a weekly boarder with her – she had been thinking of doing this with two or three children from some time. For David to be able to attend Swann School again would be a delight after all he had suffered, but it was not without problems. It was important that David should remain part of the family, so Mary undertook to drive him to school on Mondays and then return to Cadiz. On Thursdays she drove up again to collect him for the weekend. As it is four or five hours' journey each way, this is a lot of driving. For several weeks it became the routine, but Mary was not happy about the hours David was having to spend in the car. Resourceful as ever, she found out that the little house which they had previously rented was still free, and she arranged for them to be able to have it at weekends. For David it was the very best possible solution as there was more time for family life, but for Robert and Mary it was not so good. Robert had very little free time. If he had not finished work in time to go with Mary at the weekend to pick David up from school, then Mary and David spent the weekend together and Robert spend his weekend alone. This was an enormous sacrifice to make, but they did it willingly because of their concern and love for David.

This way of life continued for Mary, Robert and David for the next year. It wasn't easy for them because it meant that they were seldom ever all together. The cost of petrol was an added burden, and was certainly not covered by the small allowance they were given from David's fund. Very often Mary paid for David's books, school fees, and living-in fees before the money was refunded to her. Because she wanted to spend as much time as possible with David, she had to leave Cadiz on Thursday and not return until the following Monday. This meant that it was impossible for her to have a job. Mary and Robert did not have to undertake all the things they did for David but they always acted in his best interests and without any thought of payment.

By April 1982, Mary and I were once again having long telephone conversations concerning David's welfare. The state of affairs with regard to adoption remained static. All relevant papers had been lodged with lawyers but nothing was happening. In spite of the fact that David was very happy at Swann School, both Mary and Robert were concerned at the lack of stability of the family situation. They felt that the lack of a consistent day-to-day home-type discipline was beginning to cause deterioration in David's behaviour and attitudes. It is essential that school children have their days run along firm and consistent guidelines, but it is at home that they should, and must, be taught to live in a principled and moral way. Mary and Robert felt their influence on David was too tenuous. They even felt that it might be better for David to be permanently at boarding school than to have the unsettling pattern of school during the week and home at the weekend with perhaps only one parent.

Love, security, and consistency are prime necessities for David. If Ian believed that the reconstruction of his face could not yet withstand the winter in Minnesota, then we would have to consider the possibility of sending him to boarding school. I really couldn't bear the thought of this, but I wanted Ian to make the right decision. Not to do so might mean that David would lose all that he had already gained. When I picked up David in London I told Mary that we would make no decisions until Ian had undertaken some further surgery and was better able to judge the ability of the tissues to survive.

To our infinite relief and delight, Ian was satisfied and confident that David had reached a stage where he would not be at any great risk in Minnesota as long as we took extreme care to see that his face was protected from the cold at all times. This enabled us to make the decision that David's future would once again be with us. It was rather a bitter-sweet time because, happy as I was to have David back, I knew that it meant sadness for Robert and Mary. However, their main aim has always been to do what is best for David.

Robert and Mary played a great part in David's life and he loves them very much. We explained to him as simply as possible the changes that were planned. He had missed his brother and sisters and was very happy to be a permanent member of the family again, but when he understood that he would not now be living with Mary and Robert his concern for them was quite moving. He asked me if I thought they would be lonely without a little boy, and he wondered if they might get another one. We hope that they will always be a part of David's life. Without Mary and Robert we could never have given David the love and security he needed at the time when we had to separate from him. I am sure that when he is a young man he will recognise all they did for him and he will be proud to have been part of their lives.

David is now with us in Rochester leading a normal life just as any other little boy – apart from the continuing periods in the operating theatre!

IX
SURGICAL SAGA

Reconstruction of the defect David had involves multi-stage procedures extending over many years. The reason for this is two-fold;
firstly, tissue (meaning flesh, skin and bone) must be moved slowly
and carefully in order to maintain the blood supply; secondly, the
growth factor must be considered. Complex reconstructions using
skin and bone do not tend to grow at the same rate as normal tissue.
Because of this growth deficiency, further surgery will be necessary
until late adolescence.

Ian analysed the problem very carefully, taking photographs and
X-rays; this included a special type of X-ray called a cephalogram,
which showed very clearly the relationship of the almost absent upper
jaw to the lower jaw. We could see that David had lost all of his palate
(roof of mouth), his upper lip, and his nose, but the tremendous bony
deficiency of his upper jaw presented a horrendous problem. Ian
drew on the photographs, made diagrams of surgical procedures and
planned out the various stages of surgery. Most of all he studied
David. Whenever he was home with us and playing with the children,
I could see him mentally measuring and calculating what he might be
able to do. He said that each time he looked at the defect it seemed to
become bigger and more complex. He felt progressively more
inadequate to deal with the problem.

Dr Khursheed Moos, chief of the Oral Surgery Department in
Canniesburn Hospital, was a great help. He examined David, made
many excellent treatment suggestions, offered to help with the
surgery in any way possible, and was generally of great moral support
to Ian at that time. He, like Ian, had never seen such an enormous
defect in such a little child before.

When Ian examined David in detail he realised what a daunting
task it would be to reconstruct that ravaged face. All of the nose had
been destroyed including the septum – this is the central division
inside the nose; the bone of the upper jaw was missing between the
mid-cheek level on both sides; because of that, there was no gum, and
certainly no teeth; he had no palate and no upper lip (photos 2–4).

David has enormous dark brown eyes, and to the onlooker it

almost seemed as though his face consisted of only his eyes! Because of all the missing tissue, he could bring his lower lip right up to touch his forehead, between his eyes. I have already described my first sight of David in Charlie's office: he was sucking a lollipop and the stick, clamped between his lower teeth and his forehead, appeared to be coming right out through his forehead. In addition to tissue being missing, there was also scarring and shortening of the skin; for example, the measurement from the top of the hole between the eyes and the lower lip was half the normal distance, or less. Ian thought that the first thing to do was to lengthen the edges of the hole; this relatively small procedure would allow him to see how David would react to surgery, and to general anaesthesia.

The day to begin the reconstruction arrived and I was very apprehensive; I wanted so much for everything to go well both for Ian and for David. Ian told me that one of the most uncomfortable moments in his life was when he had to make that first incision. He probably did not appreciate it but I am sure that was when the parent-doctor conflict began.

The tight little scarred edges of the hole were released and a skin graft from the leg was taken and sutured into the raw area. When David was asleep and Ian and Dr Moos examined the pathetic little face, they became totally despondent about the task before them. I explained earlier that David did not do at all well following this procedure, and unfortunately neither did his skin graft. It failed almost completely. Ian was devastated; the first operation – a minor one – had been a failure.

Following this, David had no further surgery for many weeks, and Ian spent long hours contemplating the problem and worrying about the failures of the first procedure. Uppermost in his mind was the question of whether he should use the new speciality of microsurgery. He decided against this because, at that time, the method was unreliable and he did not dare lose a large amount of tissue. He also had the worry of trying to telescope the treatment since we had no idea of how we could finance the surgery and the cost of the hospital care. Yet for David, the best chance of successful reconstruction would be for the work to be spread over a long period. An enormous weight was lifted from Ian's shoulders when the magnificent response of the people of Glasgow to David's plight began to build up. As the fund increased so the pressure on Ian to perform the surgery rapidly disappeared. It was marvellous. Now he could modify his plans and proceed at a slower, safer pace.

The next few operations accomplished two significant steps. Skin was taken from above David's eyebrows and inserted into the sides of the facial defect to accomplish what the skin graft from the leg had failed to do – lengthen the face. These little flaps of skin were not lifted and moved in one procedure. There were two stages – this is called 'delaying a flap'. In this process the area of skin to be moved is raised up off its original site, leaving it attached at two edges, so that the vessels and nerves of the other two edges are cut. The flap is then sewn back down again, but it will now survive with a lesser blood supply than previously. After perhaps ten days it will be raised again and separated completely except for one edge. It can now be swung into the area where it is needed. It is very necessary to be sure, when one raises a flap like this, that it will be long enough to stretch to the area where it is needed. This is why Ian was always making measurements, with his handkerchief taking the place of the flap. (These small flaps are called Schmidt flaps as they were first described by Professor Edouard Schmidt, a friend and colleague of Ian's from Stuttgart.) At the same time, a larger flap was being prepared in the groin. This was a technique which was devised some years before by Ian, and Ian McGregor, one of his colleagues in Canniesburn. The groin flap was eventually to become David's nose. In addition to skin and flesh, bone from the underlying hip was included in the flap. This flap was delayed and at a later stage raised. At this time it was left in position, joined to the abdomen at two ends with the edges of the middle piece rolled over like a sausage and sewn together. This is called a tube pedicle (photos 5 and 6).

The next priority was to separate the nose and the mouth, but how? It was something Ian had never had to do before, and he knew that it had never been described in the plastic surgery literature. To be a good plastic surgeon, in addition to technical expertise, one should have a creative mind – I think that Ian, by his contributions to the speciality over the years, has proved that he does have this. He put that creativity to use at that time and made his plan. He delayed a flap of skin on the forehead with its base at the top of the nose and its upper end towards the hairline (photo 7). After ten days, the flap was raised and swung down so that the base was still intact. The flap was then turned around and sutured inside the hole in the face to an incision that had been made where the level of the roof of the mouth would be (photo 8). The edges of the defect left on the forehead were able to be moved together and sutured. This has left only a fine white scar on David's forehead. The raw undersurface of the flap was

1 David, wearing his Peruvian hat, soon
after his arrival in Scotland in 1977

2
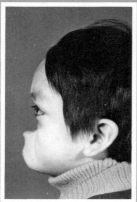

3
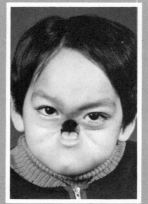

4
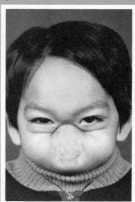

5
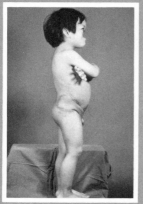

6

7
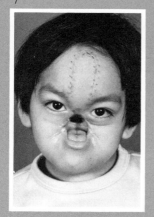

8

2, 3 & 4 Show the defect
of David's face on his
arrival in Scotland

5 & 6 Show the tube
pedicle raised but still
in position on the groin

7 Flap of skin on the
forehead

8 After ten days the
skin is raised, turned
down into position and
sutured inside the hole

9

10

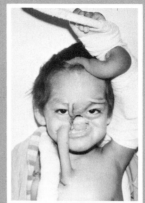

11

9 David's arm becomes
the 'carrier' for the tube
pedicle

10 The pedicle in place
on his head and the
supportive metal frame

11 Airbag body splint.
The splint filled with air
keeps the body
immobile so the risk of
tearing a flap is reduced

12

13

14

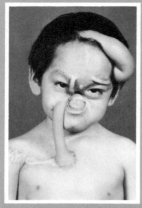
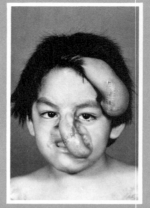
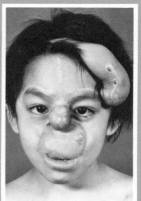

15

16

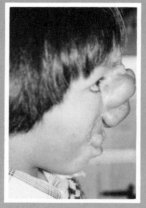
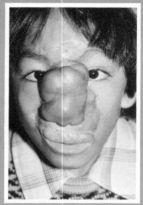

12 The tube pedicle 'parked' on David's head; the small Schmidt flaps in different stages and the deltopectoral flaps

13 & 14 The flaps which were used to release and lengthen the cheeks; lengthen the

palate; provide cover for the bone grafts which would form the upper jaw; form the bulk of cheeks and lip and provide lining for the nose

15 & 16 The pedicle in position as David's nose

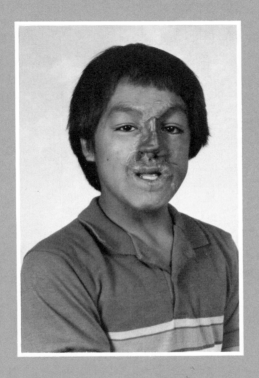

17 David in September 1984

18

19

20 ·

18 On holiday at 'the wee house'

19 In spite of arm tied to groin, David rides his bicycle

20 'There were many times when David did not look at all good . . . to see
Jane hug and kiss him . . . was really quite moving'

21 Outside Granny's house in 1981

22

23

22 & 23 In the Botanic
Gardens, Glasgow:
(above) with Jane and
Philip

VIII

24

25

24 With Robert and
Mary in Spain

25 Playing with friends
in Spain

26

27

26 Sister Seta, Father Severino, Mother Amalia with Marjorie in Lima

27 Marjorie, Padre Castillo, Flori and mission children

X

28

29

30

28 & 29 David's mother and father

30 Marjorie with David's natural parents

31

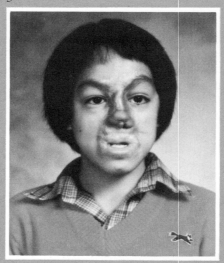

32

31 In Rochester, Minnesota. Bamber
Valley School's fifth grade in 1984

32 David, September 1983

33

34

Adoption party

33 'I'm safe now, Mum'

34 Cutting the celebration cake. Linda
is looking on

35

36

35 Ian, Marjorie and David with Cardinal Landazuri

36 Playing cards with Ian

Christmas 1984

37 Opening gifts with Andrew and Susan

38 David, Linda and Sarah. By the look on Linda's face David is cheating again!

39 Ski-ing with Linda
and Ian

40 New bike: Christmas
1984

covered with a skin graft taken from David's thigh. Anyone who has had a skin graft taken knows very well that the donor site, or place from which the skin is taken, can be very painful for quite a while – David was no exception to this. After two weeks, the base of the flap on the forehead was divided and the skin graft was removed. The remainder of the flap was turned down and sutured to the part forming the mouth side of the palate – something like a sandwich. David now had a palate, or separation between his nasal cavity and the cavity of his mouth. This helped him in two respects, when he was eating and when he was trying to speak.

We had always been amazed at David's ability to eat more or less anything placed in front of him. He used his tongue rather like a cement-mixer, placing the food underneath then mashing it up and swallowing it in one gulp. This is not a wonderful process for one's digestion, but nevertheless he survived! In order to drink, he simply held his head back and, literally, poured the liquid down his throat. It was not a pleasant performance to watch and on two occasions when we took the children to a restaurant to eat – they always considered this a special treat – it was made very clear that we were not welcome with David. On one occasion we were told that they no longer served children in the evening, and on the other it was only too obvious that the quicker we ate and left the better! Both of these places were casual, informal eating places where we had eaten as a family in the past. We are very fortunate, however, to have friends who cared more about a little boy's happiness than losing a few customers. For some time before David was part of the family, Ian and I had gone to the Pendulum Restaurant, in West Princes Street, when any special occasion came along. Ilario, the owner, and Marino, his manager, proved to be not only wonderful friends to us but also to David. When they heard that we could no longer take the family out to eat if we had David with us, they assured us that we were welcome to bring all the children there at any time. For them the Pendulum Restaurant was really a treat! Ilario, Marino, Fiona (the bartender!), the chef and the waiters were all terrific. They always arranged a table so that David could not be observed and took great pleasure in making our evenings most enjoyable.

The tube pedicle on David's right groin, after ten days, was cut free at its outer end, and that end was sewn on to David's left wrist. His arm was to act as what plastic surgeons term a 'carrier' (photo 9). This transfer of tissue was something Ian had never carried out on such a small child before, and he was fairly apprehensive, particularly since communicating with David was not easy. It would have been so much more difficult without Mary and Robert.

For three to four weeks the pedicle was attached to David's left arm and thus his arm movements were exceedingly limited. To curb his exuberance, and prevent him tearing the flap from his abdomen, we had to secure his arm to his body by means of a bandage. This he did not appreciate at all.

After another four weeks the pedicle was detached from the abdomen, but still attached to his wrist. Normally this flap containing bone would have been placed directly on to the nose area. In David's case, however, there was still a lot of preparation to be done. First it was decided to 'park' the flap on David's scalp, and thus it was sutured on to his head. This meant, as can be seen in the photograph, that his arm was in a very unnatural position, and it would have been impossible for him to have kept it there without some kind of support. Without help he would have torn the pedicle off his head very quickly. Initially, when he was in the hospital, he was in bed and the pedicle was kept in position with pads and bandages. When he came home, however, he expected to be allowed to run around and play outside just as he usually did, and this presented a big problem! Enter Robert, the engineer.

Robert finds it very hard to see David in hospital, especially when he is suffering a lot of pain, but when it comes to the practicalities of holding up an arm, that is a different matter altogether! He studied the problem, made a few drawings and then very cleverly constructed a tubular metal frame which curved around David's back, was tied with bandages at the front and supported the outer aspect of his arm. Although well designed, for David it was very uncomfortable. The frame had to be kept on his body and arm by means of bandages (photo 10). During the day it was not too bad, because he had many things to take his mind off the discomfort. At night, however, he got hot, and his arm and body became 'itchy'. No matter how he lay, the frame seemed to cut into him, and his arm and shoulder ached. He and I spent many sleepless nights, rearranging bandages, and trying to get to the itchy places with a knitting needle – I think we also must have created a record in our use of talcum powder! Normally this situation would have lasted three weeks before the pedicle was divided from his wrist, but Ian was being cautious in the extreme; he wanted to be very sure that the end attached to David's scalp was really secure and providing a good source of nourishment for the pedicle, so he left it like that for another week. That was a long month! It was really quite funny to see David wearing his frame and running around playing football with Andrew. Everything comes to an end, however, and the pedicle was taken off his wrist and sewn on to his scalp a little behind the other end. For the first time for many nights David and I slept all throught the night. Now his head looked as though it had a handle!

The next surgical project was to release the insides of the cheeks, lengthen the palate further, and make an upper lip. The defect was still enormous in spite of all the work that had been done.

Flaps, which would again be formed into 'sausages', were outlined on David's chest. These stretched from the midline of his upper chest out to the points of his shoulders. They are called deltopectoral flaps and were designed initially by Dr Bakamjian in Buffalo, New York, with whom Ian had spent some time during his early training in plastic surgery. The flaps were delayed and then the shoulder ends were taken up to the face. One flap was used to supply tissue to free up the inside of the cheeks, to lengthen the palate, and to provide cover for the upper gum, or alveolar, area. The other flap was also prepared and taken up to the face in a different series of operations. It was used to form the bulk of the upper lip and cheeks; some of the remainder of the flap was taken up to the nose area where it would eventually be used as lining for the new nose (photo 12).

All of this was time-consuming. Probably the most frustrating aspect of such a monumental amount of reconstructive surgery is the time that has to be devoted to waiting and allowing the newly formed reconstruction to settle. In addition the areas which have been deprived of bone and soft tissue must be allowed to heal. It is unwise to perform early surgery on a newly reconstructed area because the blood supply will not be adequately established. It takes many months before subsequent surgery can be undertaken safely.

David's body now had so many scars from the procedures already carried out that it was rather like a 'map' of his surgical history! His thighs bore the scars where the skin grafts had been taken, there was a scar in his groin, a scar on his wrist, and scars on his chest. They mark the sacrifices which have had to be made in order to give him a face.

Many small procedures had to be carried out from time to time. They were necessary to rearrange the skin, to remove fat from some of the bulky areas of the initial reconstruction, and to close any small holes between the nose and the mouth. These holes occur at areas where one flap joins another.

The next project in the overall plan was a most hazardous one and

Ian was not at all sure that it would be successful, either in the short term or in the long term. He wanted to begin building the skeleton of the face. This involved placing bone between the layers of the new palate and the new upper gum. In addition the cheek area would be built up.

Three ribs were removed and split along their length with a hammer and chisel to give more available bone. Afterwards the rib cavity was carefully sutured and in time the ribs will re-form again. The split ribs were placed between the layers of gum and palate and wired to the tiny pieces of bone which were all that remained of David's upper jaw; other portions were placed on the front of the upper jaw area to give more emphasis to his cheeks. All the indications from previous research, from Ian's own experience and discussions with other plastic surgeons, were that this procedure would fail, the grafts would melt away and, without support, David's face would once again take on its squashy, rubbery appearance. Another fear of Ian's was that the skin covering the bone grafts would die because of poor blood supply. In spite of this gloomy prognosis, David sailed through this surgery and never looked back; the skin caused no problem and until this day the grafts have survived solidly. Within a few days we saw David running around the garden playing football with Andrew. Every time he kicked the ball he would hold his chest and groan as he felt the pain but nothing would stop him. Andrew came in for quite a bit of lecturing because I accused him of encouraging David to play before he was ready. However, I overheard David pleading with Andrew: 'Please Andrew – just five minutes, Mum won't notice.' Such was David's determination and personality. I feel that it is this stubborn streak which always keeps him going when things get really rough!

The time was finally approaching when it seemed that David would get what he wanted more than anything in the world – a nose! He really had been patient. We had always spent a great deal of time explaining to him exactly what each procedure entailed, why it was necessary, and what it would mean to him in terms of pain. In this way he never wakened up after an operation to the shock of pain he had not known about, or to find some new arrangement of his body for which he was not prepared. The pedicle on David's head had been there for months – longer than it should have been and much longer than Ian would have liked. At times Ian was unsure of what he should or could do, thus some stages of the reconstruction were ready to be used sooner than planned. So it was with the 'nose'; it was prepared and ready to be moved long before the face was ready to take it.

Due to the length of time the pedicle had to remain on David's head, we learned that newly reconstructed tissue does not react well to cold. At one point during the winter months, we left our little household in the capable hands of Granny and Aunt May while Ian and I were attending a plastic surgery meeting. David had come to enjoy these times as much as his brother and sisters. He said that Granny always wanted to play cards with him – Andrew said it was great because Granny always sewed the buttons on his shirt and Mum did not! When we returned I noticed that there was a small area in the centre of the pedicle which was white in the middle and a little black around the edges. Ian immediately thought of frostbite; this was confirmed when we found out that the first snowfall of the year had occurred during our absence and David had persuaded his sisters to take him out to make a snowman! This told us that although the temperature was above zero, the blood supply to the flap was not sufficient to nourish its centre in the damp, bone-chilling cold of Glasgow. It was this which made Ian apprehensive about how the reconstruction would stand up to the severe Minnesota winters. This story also had a funny side to it. After the frostbite incident the problem was how to keep the sausage-like pedicle warm. We tried all kinds of hats, but they always seemed to slip and expose a part of the pedicle. Finally the girls came up with a solution. They knitted little scarves and we wrapped them round the pedicle. David, unlike Joseph, did not have a coat of many colours, but he had a different multicoloured scarf every day, thanks to his sisters! One other amusing incident arose from this pedicle. After having been at playschool once or twice David was beginning to know the little songs that were sung there and he said to me one day: 'I'm a bit like the little teapot in the song, Mum, I've got a real handle but no spout!'

The flap on his head was laboriously moved in several stages, with approximately three weeks separating each stage. Eventually it was taken down to the face; at this time, however, it was a parody of a nose. Having waited for this event for so long, I have to pay tribute to David for his strength of character and sense of humour in the way in which he accepted the huge, awful-looking potato-like thing on his face, which we had the nerve to call a nose! He is a great little boy, and he listened patiently while Ian explained that it would not always look like that, but it would take a great deal more time before he could improve it (photos 13–16).

Several additional procedures were necessary to de-fat the flap, trim the extra skin and try to form the complicated anatomy of the lower nose. The skin of the deltopectoral, or chest, flap which had been put on the nasal area was used to line the nose. Rubber tubes were placed inside the nose to maintain the nostril openings. Later, after his treatment in Rochester had begun, these were changed for small silicone tubes made by Dr Laney, the maxillofacial prosthodontist. These were kept in position for a long period of time, to prevent shrinkage and closure of the nostrils. Once again Robert's engineering skill was of great importance. David was wearing the tubes when he was living with Mary and Robert in Spain. It is extremely difficult to design a secure method of retaining such tubes in children; in this case we chose a kind of spring-clip system, but if this was too tight, destruction of tissue between the tubes might have occurred. For one reason or another David frequently lost the tubes – swimming, playing football, or, on at least one occasion, letting them disappear down the drain as he washed them! The first time the tubes were lost we asked Mary to take David to see Dr Jaime Planas, a plastic surgeon in Barcelona. He had already seen David on several occasions in our home and understood exactly what the problem was. Unhappily his technicians were unable to produce tubes suitable for David. The ones they made were too large and extremely unsightly because they fitted on with a clip which resembled a large safety-pin! Quite rightly, Mary and Robert thought that to wear them would cause David to be ridiculed and that it was too much to expect. As quickly as possible we sent Robert some of the silicone tubing used by Dr Laney and he fashioned another set of tubes for David. He had to do this several times; it was very fortunate for David that Robert was an engineer.

Ian had now reached a stage when some of the body scars had matured and he tried to improve on their appearance by excising them and closing the incisions very carefully. Unfortunately David's brown skin does not form good scars. I had to massage the new scars three times a day with a type of cortisone cream, in an attempt to have the best possible result – I frequently tell Ian that the surgery is the easiest part of looking after David!

David's nose had now to be left to settle, and Ian's attention was once again directed to the upper lip. I knew he thought about it a great deal and was greatly frustrated because he was unsure of how to make it look better. I have always taken a great interest in Ian's work, and at one time I drew the diagrams for some of the papers he was writing about cleft lip and palate. I tease him a lot about his results and David also loves to do that! It was very hard to see him worry so much over what to do. He has never been able to treat people simply as problems, he has always become emotionally involved with them. With David, however, there was one significant difference: the problem was always there, at the hospital and at home.

I remembered reading in some of Ian's publications that skin from the tongue had been used to resurface or repair a lip, and I asked him why he didn't do that for David. He explained that it had always been the lower lip which had been involved and that he had never used the procedure in a child as young as David. I have to admit that I kept pushing him about it, constantly pointing out that David's mouth looked very odd because his upper lip was all the same colour instead of having a pink border. Finally he allowed himself to be persuaded into trying. This, however, must have been one of the most painful and uncomfortable procedures that David had to endure, and as I sat beside him in Canniesburn some hours after surgery I felt thoroughly miserable for having suggested it. Poor David seemed to be more upset than I had ever seen him. He had difficulty in breathing through his nose and now most of his mouth had been closed by suturing the tongue on to the upper lip. Ian had thought about this problem and in an attempt to alleviate it had sewn large rubber tubes to the lower lip on either side of the tongue. These protruded out of his mouth like two pipes and did enable him to breathe a little more easily. The pain and the difficulty in breathing made him restless and if he began to cry we thought that there would be a distinct tendency for him to tear the tongue off his lip. At last, after some sedation, he settled down. When the Sister in charge of the ward came back on duty we discovered that there was a very good reason for him having had such pain. Quite by mistake one of the auxiliary nurses had given him grapefruit juice to drink instead of water. She had no idea of how raw the inside of his mouth was and how much pain that would cause him.

Finally, after ten days, the tongue flap was divided and part of David's tongue became his upper lip! Ian also worked a little on the corners of his mouth and the final result was really very good. David studied the result in the mirror and pronounced the job to be satisfactory because he could now give 'real kisses'!

This basically ends the Glasgow part of David's surgical saga. During this time, he was being examined from time to time by the Orthodontic Department, the Dental Department and by Khursheed Moos in the Oral Surgery Department. Nurses, radiographers, secretaries, ward maids, and orderlies, in both Canniesburn Hospital and the Nuffield McAlpin Clinic, came to know David and admire his courage. He became a symbol for other patients, young and old; they were encouraged and heartened by his attitude to the pain and suffering which he had to endure. Many have said they became better persons for having known David.

Without the co-operation of two superb anaesthetists, Dr Duncan Ferguson and Dr Douglas Arthur, Ian would never have been able to effect such a successful reconstruction. David presented some very difficult anaesthetic problems, but 'Uncle Duncan' and Douglas Arthur accepted this challenge and always made things as easy as possible for him.

The Nuffield McAlpin Clinic, owned by the Nuffield Trust, is a private institution which opened its doors and its heart to David. They were always ready to bend the rules a little for him, and tried as best they could to fit in his surgery whenever Ian was able to do it. Never at any time did they charge for any service given for David, for use of the operating theatre, or for his stay in the Clinic. There was no reason why they should not have charged; they knew we had to pay fees to the National Health Service, and they knew that the people of Glasgow had raised money for David's medical expenses, but they did not. It was a warm and wonderful gesture and one which we appreciate very much. It was a special treat for David being in a room by himself and having a television – needless to say, he was thoroughly spoiled by everyone.

For David, coming to Rochester for surgery meant facing a new and much more formal system. St Mary's Hospital, where Ian operates, dwarfs Canniesburn and the Nuffield McAlpin Clinic put together! The Mayo Clinic complex, which is separate from the hospitals, is an imposing collection of buildings. Gone were the days of early-morning premedication and Uncle Duncan. David was entering a totally different world and of course he was very apprehensive.

There were new names for him to learn. Dr Howard Sather, an orthodontist; Dr William Laney, a prosthodontist; and Dr Gene Keller, an oral surgeon. In the early days Dr Jesse Muir was the anaesthetist who became known to David and he was very understanding of David's fears and did his best to reassure him. More recently Dr John McMichan and Dr Brian Dawson have been anaesthetising David. John is Australian and Brian is English and both are familiar with terms like 'trolley' instead of cart, and injection instead of 'shot' – this helps David to feel more at home! Many people are surprised that David still has an awful dread of being 'put to sleep'. In spite of the numerous times he has gone through the process he has never lost his apprehension. I greatly appreciate the kindness and compassion shown to David by all of these people.

Ian has also had the benefit of the moral support and medical expertise of his colleagues in the plastic surgery department at the Mayo Clinic. All of them, Dr John Woods, Dr George Irons, Dr P. G. Arnold, and Dr Jack Fisher have been encouraging and enthusiastic about Ian's struggle with David's reconstruction. They have always been ready to give advice when asked and are very interested in David as a person. I sometimes think that they are even more proud of his numerous sporting achievements than we are!

After a completely fresh assessment by the craniofacial team David began his first summer programme of surgery in Rochester. Very quickly his two stuffed animals, Henry the dog and Ruby Rabbit, became known to the nursing staff on the paediatric floor at St Mary's. Ian's plan that first summer was to thin and refine his nose and insert more bone grafts into the upper jaw to keep its growth up to that of the lower jaw. Dr Keller was to perform some surgery on the roof of the mouth to flatten it out in preparation for a denture at some time in the future.

The surgery was accomplished in several procedures. Again there was considerable pain and discomfort, especially from the hip where the bone graft was taken. At this time it was noticed that David's lack of success in breathing through his nose was basically because it lacked support; this allowed the nostrils to collapse. Dr Laney made the small silicone tubes which I have already described, and these helped this situation considerably. It was during this summer that Ian did a procedure encouraged by David himself! David had several times mentioned that his ears stuck out too much, and Ian agreed with him. I felt that in relation to everything being done, this was unnecessary. David and his dad, however, put their heads together and came up with the solution. I was told that the cartilage taken out of the ears would be useful for support in another area of his reconstruction. With such determination, how could I stop them. In retrospect it really was a good decision because David undoubtedly did look better. David went back to Spain shortly after this procedure.

To have David coming back and forth for surgery was difficult for many reasons but not least for Mary and Robert. There were times when he returned with his wounds not completely healed and after procedures which caused Ian some worry because there was still a chance of complications occurring. A factor of great importance in David's life is to be as normal as possible. Because of this we did not want him to miss any schooling unnecessarily and so we waited until his school year was finished before we brought him to Rochester. Ian tried to accomplish as much as possible within the weeks he was with us. Usually, however, he was not sufficiently recovered to go back for the start of the school term. Consequently he missed two or three weeks. It was a huge responsibility for Mary and Robert having him back when he had not completely recovered from his surgery. They had to take over the care of his surgical wounds, gently ease him back into their routine, and make the decision about when to send him back to school.

When David returned the following summer he looked much better; his swelling had settled down and his scars were more mature. Very quickly surgery began again; Ian was always keen to begin so that everything might be well healed before he had to return.

This time further procedures were undertaken to bone-graft the upper gum and jaw. The skin of the nose was contoured a little more, and the facial scars were revised. Again we went through the days of bruising and swelling, then suture removal with the usual discomfort of that procedure. I have mentioned the many things I have learned since becoming the mother of a child with facial deformity. Initially the reasons for taking David out of hospital so quickly after surgery were to save expense and to help him feel secure, but it also meant learning to nurse a patient after surgery. I had to clean the suture-lines properly, take care of the reconstructed area, and clean out and keep the suction drains flowing. There is a great deal of post-operative pain following the removal of ribs or bone from the hip so lifting or moving David had to be done with a great deal of care to avoid causing additional pain. I have never had any formal nursing training – my experiences with David are the total extent of my nursing career. Looking after one's children when they have the usual childish ailments is not at all the same thing. I have often wondered, since taking care of David, how I could ever have thought it difficult when the others were sick!

Once again Helen Baird, Sister in charge of the paediatric wards, was a great help. She always made time to answer any of my questions about any aspect of nursing David. One of David's little fears is that of having the tape removed from the suture lines. Before Ian removed the sutures, I always put David in a bath, then he and I would gently work the tape off. Ian had to pretend to be surprised when he was presented with a wound free of tape! On one occasion he laughingly said to David, 'Since you and your mother are so clever I should make her take your stitches out!' David very seriously and quietly replied, 'I would like that, Dad, Mum is more gentle than you.' That was my first lesson on suture removal. Now it is simply routine!

With surgery over for another year, and David back on the road to recovery, I had once again to make the sad journey with him to Spain.

In the summer of 1982 Ian worked with Dr Keller to define the upper gum and to trim and contour the upper lip. The nose was supported with a bone graft from the skull, a technique which Ian has developed. This type of bone survives better, the donor site is not painful, and the scar, being within the hairline, is not seen.

Since then there have been several other operations. The nose has been lengthened using a flap from behind the ear. In this procedure all of the skin behind the ear was taken on a strip of scalp and sutured into the nose. For three weeks poor David had to go around with a portion of his scalp, complete with hair, running across his cheek! This I have to admit was entirely my fault. Normally, to make it easier for the surgeon, their hair is shaved from the flap before it is lifted, but as we had planned a summer holiday for David immediately after surgery, I persuaded Ian not to do that. We thought that David really needed an old-fashioned holiday playing on the beach in the good sea air. As usual time was short and we did not want him to miss school, as would have been necessary if we had waited for the hair to grow before we set off. If the flap had been shaved he would have had a large bald area on the side of his head and David has enough problems without this – especially on holiday. During the time the flap was covering his face, complete with hair, I managed to make it look not too bad by putting vaseline on the hair and tucking it under the flap!

The upper jaw was again bone-grafted to build it up further and keep pace with general facial growth. Ian took a wedge out of David's lower lip; this segment of lower lip was swung up into the upper lip to increase its size. This greatly improved his profile because the lower lip has always been too prominent. The blood supply to this wedge-shaped segment was maintained intact for approximately ten days, until the lower lip tissue developed a supply from the upper lip. During this time David's lips were sewn together and I could only feed him liquids through a straw which I placed in a small space left at one corner of his mouth. I think being unable to eat is the aspect of surgery David hates most. Pain he can put up with – lack of food – no!

A new name now enters the saga, that of Professor Per-Ingvar Branemark of Göteborg, Sweden. For seventeen or eighteen years this ingenious orthopaedic surgeon has been working on the insertion of metal posts into bone to establish a permanent fixture for dentures. Others have tried this in the past but without consistent success. Professor Branemark has achieved the apparently impossible – successful metal implantation into bone – osteo-integrated prosthesis.

Ian heard of Professor Branemark's interesting research work while we were living in Sweden. At that time he was inserting the metal prostheses into dogs and achieving remarkable long-term results. Because of the potential significance of this work for facial reconstruction, Ian followed its progress and was delighted when the Mayo Clinic invited the professor to Rochester. He immediately thought how wonderful it would be if Professor Branemark could offer any help with David and his toothless upper jaw.

Professor Branemark is a delightful man who is totally enthusiastic about his work. I took David to see him when he first came to Rochester in 1983, and after an extensive study of X-rays and examination of David, he was very hopeful as to what might be achieved. He proposed operating on David when he came back in 1984 and we were very happy about this.

That great day has come and gone; Ian opened up David's face and exposed all the bone which he has been carefully grafting into position over the last seven years. Professor Branemark was delighted with the bone-graft situation, as was Ian, and together they worked on David in this first surgery which has set the stage for him eventually to have a dental bridge constructed. David was eight hours in the operating room on this occasion. A large amount of carefully shaped bone was taken from his hip and securely screwed on to the existing bone with a special type of metal screw. Another portion of the hip-bone was used to further build up and lengthen his nose. The plan was that some weeks after surgery, when the bone graft to the mid-face was secure, the central core of the screws would be removed and metal pegs screwed in their place. These pegs would provide supporting foundation for a permanent tooth-bearing bridge. For David, after his nose, teeth were what he wanted most.

Unfortunately, this operation was not successful for David. The bone graft in the upper jaw became infected and Ian had to make the very difficult decision to have it taken out so that there would be no damage to the good bone already in his jaw and nose. It was with a very heavy heart that I explained to David what would have to be done. I told him how upset and disappointed Ian was and, although he was not at all happy about going back into hospital for more surgery, David said: 'Tell Dad not to worry, Mum – as long as I can keep my nose, it's OK.'

Surgery for David will go on until his late teenage years and Ian has already planned what he would like to accomplish for him. His nose can be greatly improved using skin from his forehead, but Ian does not want to use this until late adolescence. He would like to give him a moustache, using a scalp flap. This would cover his upper lip which otherwise will always be rather ugly and scarred. There will probably be more bone-grafting to his face and perhaps forward movement of the upper jaw and backward movement of the lower jaw by surgical means, to give a better profile. The latter is a big operation but usually gives spectacular results. The decision about this will depend on how David's face grows.

One very heart-warming experience has been the attitude of David's classmates to his most recent surgery. Usually we try to keep surgery for the summer months when he is not at school, but this time it was necessary to have it done when Professor Branemark was in Rochester. Each child in the class made a card for David, and each had some special thing to tell him about how courageous they thought he was, how much they missed him, and how much they were looking forward to seeing what had been done. It is marvellous to see such spontaneous love and support from these children. It reminded me very much of the hundreds of cards that the schoolchildren in Glasgow made for David after Edward Miller sent a letter to all the schools explaining about David and how he needed help to get a face. These children sent their pocket-money to David's fund, and they made beautiful cards and pictures for him. I still have them, so that some day David will understand what a lot of love he received from children who had never seen him, and probably never would.

David's surgery, and how he has reacted to this epic of pain and suffering, has been an example to everyone with whom he has come in contact. But he is not unique in this. During the years of surgery David has gone through, I have met many of my husband's craniofacial patients who are all equally brave. As their mothers, we are constantly astounded at the courage and endurance shown by our children and we have learned much from them.

David trusts the doctors and nurses who give their best in skill and compassion. He has had many disappointments as well as successes and he has accepted them, just as he accepts his deformity and the need to get on with life in spite of it. What a contrast to the adults one hears of who, rather than draw on their own inner will to survive and progress, criticise, blame and sue the very people who are trying to help them! None of us can guarantee that our best will be good enough, but it is all we have to give.

David represents more than just a little boy with a missing face; he is a living example of faith in what other human beings are trying to do for him.

X
THE TRUTH

In the spring of 1982 Ian told me Desmond Wilcox had phoned him from England. Mr Wilcox is an experienced and well-known television producer who is probably best known for his work on the 'Man Alive' series, as well as for many excellent documentaries. He had read many of the newspaper reports about David and wanted to discuss with us the possibility of producing a documentary about him. We had had many such requests in the past, both before leaving Glasgow and after our arrival in the United States. After leaving home we continued to send back regular reports on David's surgical and social progress to the *Evening Times* newspaper and to the Archbishop's office. Apart from these, Ian and I had decided that we should shield David as much as possible from any undue publicity. We felt that the more he was in the limelight the more he might learn to depend on his deformity as a crutch in a social situation instead of learning to face up to his handicap. We also did not want him spoiled because of media exposure.

Ian and I discussed the proposal fully. We decided we did not want to take part and told Mr Wilcox of our decision. After a series of lengthy phone calls in the next few weeks, we were encouraged to reconsider. Mr Wilcox pointed out how much a television programme can achieve in arousing public interest. He argued that David's story, told sincerely and without sensationalism, would help to open up more positive attitudes towards disability of all kinds; also that it would highlight the lack of medical care in Peru. Funds are desperately needed there to treat other patients suffering from the same problems as David.

Here I must fill in the background to Ian's efforts to establish a centre for craniofacial surgery in Peru. In 1982 Ian gave a series of lectures and some practical assistance in Caracas, Venezuela, as a result of which he was made an honorary staff member of the hospital of San Juan de Dios. These hospitals, run by a religious foundation originally established in Spain, are found in many other parts of the world and there is one in Lima. Ian wrote to the director there explaining the difficulties he and Charlie had encountered in establishing a treatment centre in Peru, and was told he was welcome to work in the San Juan de Dios in Lima at any time. He has now operated on one young girl there, but there was a severe shortage of back-up facilities. Although the Brothers were happy to provide the operating theatre they had no theatre staff, monitoring equipment, or the surgical instruments required for this specialised surgery. Any way which might help to fund a treatment centre in Peru must be considered.

We were apprehensive of how a television documentary would intrude into our lives, and we were reluctant also to cause David any upset, but we had to acknowledge that the publicity could help to improve the prospects for other children like David.

We told Mr Wilcox that we were convinced of his sincerity and motives in making the programme, but that we could not agree without consulting Mary and Robert. Since they entered our lives they have become part of the family, but they are modest young people who value their privacy, and I had given my word not to give their Spanish address to anyone without their permission.

I explained the situation to Mary and related all that had taken place. She and Robert, like ourselves, thought we should allow the BBC to make the film if there was a chance that other children might be helped by it. Initially the filming was to be carried out in Spain where David was at that time, so I assured Mary that if, for any reason, they wished to cancel the arrangement they would have our full support.

We are very proud of David for the way in which he accepts his deformity. He is totally aware of how he looks but he does not dwell on it and has not become at all introspective; neither does he look for pity or sympathy. We are equally proud of his fortitude, his attitude to surgery, his sense of fun, and his loving nature. To highlight these attributes in a film where he would clearly know that he was a 'star', however, seemed to present a potentially dangerous situation. Our greatest fear was of his exposure to the limelight.

In Spain David was filmed taking part in all of his normal activities, at home, at play, at school, and in a regular visit to the market-place with Mary. This was done just as he was finishing his school year. I went over to meet Mary and David in London at the end of the school term and he and I then returned to Rochester.

British Caledonian first entered David's life in February 1977 when they flew David and Martine from Gatwick airport to Glasgow completely free of charge. Now some five years later they once again treated David kindly. Desmond arranged for him to have a tour of one of their DC10 jets. This was filmed for the documentary, and although it was interesting to see how quickly David picked up all he was shown, I think the undisguised empathy and sense of fun of Captain Adrian Ross absolutely stole the show! It was a wonderful example of how a man who knew nothing of David until just before their meeting was caught up almost immediately by the personality of the child and reacted to that rather than to his appearance.

By the time the filming began in Rochester, David knew the whole team. Besides Desmond, the presenter and producer, there was the director, Alex McCall, his assistant, Jan Riddell, two cameramen, a sound engineer and lighting man. Quite soon, Jan was well and truly wrapped round David's little finger; he was able to explain Roy's sound equipment to us and the cameras of Colin and Andrew posed no problems. The lighting man, Kenny, quickly became known as Kenny Dalgleish after David's hero – the footballer in the Glasgow Celtic team, still supported by him even in far-off Minnesota.

We were treated at all times by everyone working on the making of the documentary with consideration and courtesy. It was a very emotional and trying experience for us, but because they were such a great bunch of people to work with it was made much easier.

Having agreed to take part in the documentary, we did so as honestly as possible. There were no contrived situations and no rehearsing or staging of interviews. At times it may have seemed that Desmond was harassing me with unnecessary questions or with superfluous observations, but David's story is not a trite 'happy-ever-after' tale. Therefore it is essential to show the distressing and sad moments as well as the happy ones. I think that the true facts were shown but with sensitivity. I have never believed that it is necessary to see a person totally distraught and weeping at the scene of some personal tragedy to be able to understand their sadness and pain. Our sadness and our happiness was portrayed in a sensitive way. There were many very private emotional moments, both pre- and post-surgery for instance, which Desmond and Alex could have included in the documentary, but did not. They had given us an assurance before we began that they would not sensationalise the story by placing undue accent on any one aspect. Their aim was to show events, simply and truthfully, as they took place.

Because of the many hours spent together in discussion and the filming of David's story, inevitably, Desmond, Alex and 'the crew'

97

became part of our lives for a while. David, however, came to mean much more to them than just a job. The natural tenacity with which, through all the upset and fear of surgery, he held on to his dream of getting a nose, brought home to them how imperative it was that this courageous young boy should be given the security of a permanent home. He should not be afraid that at any time he could be sent back to Peru. The crew realised, as many people do not, that our fight to adopt David is totally for his benefit and not ours. We love David, to us he is our son, but that does not make him so in the eyes of the law, thus he has no legal status whatsoever. That is why, in the beginning, when Robert, Mary, Ian and I discussed adoption, security was more important than the decision as to who would be his adoptive parents. Out of this awareness of David's predicament and the BBC's concern for him, was born the idea of the second part of the documentary, *Marjorie's Quest*. It tells the story of the journey we made to Peru, to search for documents which might finally help to realise an adoption.

Because of the generosity of the people of Glasgow, David has never been subsidised in any way by any government in either Britain, Spain, or the United States. Yet in both the United Kingdom and the United States I have had to request regular extensions of his visa to allow him to remain in the country. Every request has to be accompanied by a letter detailing the planned surgery. If we could not prove that he was having surgery, then it could be deportation. Many people have laughed at our fears and said that he would never be sent out of the country, but none of them could give us an absolute guarantee. On one occasion when we were in the process of submitting yet another petition for a visa extension, Ian informed the American Immigration authorities that we were trying to secure a legal adoption for David. We received the extension, but there was a little footnote which said: 'Waiting for adoption is not a valid reason for keeping this child in the country.' If Ian wants to rest David's face for a year, will he be allowed to stay until he is ready for more surgery? We are fearful of the answer to that question. If Ian and I were killed in an accident, would David be considered as one of our children? Would he be allowed to stay until alternative arrangements could be made for him? Somehow we must make David as secure as our own children.

Our search for proof of David's birth was not a frivolous one. We have been told repeatedly that without a birth certificate an adoption is impossible and our experiences have confirmed this. Our decision to make the journey in search of security for David was taken only after a great deal of research and consideration of what our actions might mean to people living in a fairly isolated jungle area. We decided that as a first step we would go to Lima. When we had some established facts to work on we would decide whether or not to go further, taking advice from Peruvians who would have local knowledge.

Before Desmond could be given permission to film within Peru all the correct applications had to be made. Permission was granted, which was a little surprising, since I would have thought that to have some of the worse aspects of one's country displayed on a foreign television network might not be terribly desirable. It is amazing, however, how much more effective an organisation with a little clout can be than any individual. With the power of the BBC behind them, researchers were busily engaged on the work necessary for the documentary. Since none of us was capable of either speaking or understanding Spanish fluently, we needed an interpreter. Once again, British Caledonian became our fairy godmother! Our interpreter was Rita Lopez, wife of Carlos, who is manager of the British Caledonian office in Lima. Rita speaks both English and Spanish and was a pleasure to work with. She has a warm, calm personality and was obviously a concerned party in what we were doing, and this was reassuring.

Several appointments had been set up by the time we arrived in Lima. The Director of Hospital del Niño had agreed to be interviewed and a meeting had also been arranged with Mother Amalia of the Franciscan convent in Lima. No appointment could be made with Tierra de Los Hombres because Fernando and her husband were afraid that publicity might make people think that they were using this to their own gain. In the past few years it has come to light that there are groups of people calling themselves 'Adoption Agencies' who have, in fact, been 'selling children'. There has been a lot of concern about this, as a result of which the legitimate agencies have to be very careful in all requests for adoption, particularly those involving 'foreigners'. All this of course did nothing to facilitate our own efforts to adopt David.

The interview at the hospital produced nothing more than we already knew. The Director was obviously sincere in his desire to help, but he knew little about David's admission or of the surgeon in charge of the case at that time. He had not taken up his post as director until after David had left the hospital with Martine. The Hospital del Niño is immense, catering for the poor. Every time I have been there the admission hall has been seething with people, unimaginable confusion and noise. The administrative staff carry an enormous workload and therefore it is unreasonable to expect them to produce accurate records of one small patient admitted several years previously. At our meeting with Mother Amalia, however, in the serenity of the garden within the convent, which is in the heart of Lima, we learned many things we had previously only been able to guess at. The convent is run by Franciscan nuns, some of whom go to the Mission at Puerto Ocopa. This is the Mission at which David was apparently abandoned and from which he came to Lima. Mother Amalia was accompanied by Father Severino, a padre of the Franciscan Order, who was in nightly radio contact with the padre in Puerto Ocopa. From conversations with him, and scraps of knowledge gleaned here and there from Sisters who had worked at the Mission over the years, Father Severino and Mother Amalia managed to recreate events as they must have happened.

We learned that David had not been abandoned by his parents. His father, in a desperate bid to save his sick baby, had brought him to the Mission to seek help, and from there he had accompanied him to Lima, with the padre from the Mission. This trip was made in a small plane which provided the lifeline for the Mission with the outside world. I was really happy to know that my instincts about David's parents were correct. I had never believed that they had not cared. If that had been the case then they would not have gone to the Mission. To have let him die would have been much easier, but they did not.

David was born in the village of Shima, situated a considerable distance down-river from Puerto Ocopa, in a remote and beautiful area of the Andean jungle. He is a Campa Indian. I have not been able to find much published about the Campas but what I have read indicates that they lead a straightforward, uncomplicated life. Each village usually has an administrator, or headman. They eat what they can grow or what they can fish from the river. Their traditional clothing, a 'cushma', is made of a dark brown closely-woven material, usually worn long but with short sleeves. Those worn by men might have a V-shaped neckline but the women always have the higher oval-shaped neckline. In areas within reach of the Missions, however, Western dress, in the form of T-shirts and trousers, can now be seen – especially among the children and the men. Not a lot is known of the Campa tribes living in the truly remote areas of the jungle and Sierra.

Father Severino told us that Padre Castillo, the padre in Puerto

Ocopa, was awaiting our arrival. The padre knew of our search for the truth, and encouraged us to go there. Since their only communication was by radio receiver and transmitter, and many different matters had to be discussed, Father Severino explained that it was possible to learn only the basic facts. Armed with this information, I felt confident about taking the next, highly significant step – a visit to Puerto Ocopa.

Desmond now had the idea of appealing to Señora Violeta Belaunde, wife of the President, to assist us to adopt David. Not long before this there had been considerable publicity about the help she had given an Indian child to obtain major surgery in the United States. I already knew that she took a great interest in the affairs of sick children because she had on two occasions written to Ian thanking him for surgery he had undertaken on Peruvian children who had been sent to him at the Mayo Clinic. I thought that an interview might be impossible, but having experienced Desmond's persistence when he believes in a cause, I was willing to accept that he might just pull it off! If he could, the interest of the President's wife might just be the factor we needed to persuade the courts that David's case was outside of the normal adoption requests.

Time was our great problem, so we were very encouraged when Desmond secured an appointment with Palace officials almost immediately. They listened with interest to the reason for our request for an audience with Señora Belaunde, and said that provided it could be fitted into her schedule, she might look upon it favourably. In typical Peruvian fashion, however, there was thereafter a breakdown in communications – there were no further signs of an interview being granted. Desmond, however, does not give up easily, and his perseverance was finally rewarded when he managed to secure a time for the interview. He was told that he would have to come to the Palace that very morning in order to get confirmation of the arrangement. We were hoping that it would be just a matter of form but unfortunately it did not prove to be so. The President's aide was not in favour of the proposed interview; I imagine he felt it would be imprudent of the President's wife to be filmed giving a promise of help. There was a considerable delay while more discussions took place. It was tough for Desmond but for me the waiting was nerve-racking. As time passed our hope of meeting Señora Belaunde slowly evaporated.

If this were an old-fashioned cowboy and Indian movie, we would now be at the part where there is a blowing of bugles and the cavalry enters to save the day! The cavalry in this case was represented by Elvira's father. The previous evening he had returned to Lima from a business trip, and had visited us to find out how everything was progressing. He was disappointed by our lack of success in acquiring an audience at the Palace. He asked me if he could borrow one of the photographs I had of David before any reconstruction had taken place, because he wanted to show it to a very old friend of his. His friend was in fact the mother of Violeta Belaunde. Unknown to us, while Desmond was having a hard time trying to persuade the President's aide to change his mind, Señor Mulanovitch, Elvira's father, was pleading David's case with his old friend – rather more successfully! An unofficial telephone call was made from mother to daughter, and very soon afterwards Desmond was given the time and place for our interview. We were to see the President's wife at two o'clock that afternoon.

At first glance the Presidential Palace is an imposing building; closer examination reveals it to be like all the other buildings around the Plaza de Armas, rather grey and tired-looking. Even the Palace guards look as if they need to be laundered and stiffened up! The interview took place in a charming little courtyard and although we passed through a series of rooms to reach it, I have no clear recollection of what they looked like. I was very nervous. Not so much because of my impending interview with the first lady of Peru, but rather because I knew that the interview time was limited and I was unsure of my ability to present a clear and concise account of David's situation. I do remember how peaceful the courtyard was, there were many flowers, beautiful flowering trees, and two magnificent, curved ceramic benches depicting scenes from Don Quixote. I wondered fleetingly if those benches could have dated back to the time of Pizarro.

Señora Belaunde was charming and listened with interest as we explained the problems of obtaining an adoption certificate. She agreed that David's case was special but said she had no power to change any part of the law concerning adoption. However, if our lawyer presented all the necessary papers she promised to try to expedite matters for us. After the official interview was over she asked me many more questions about David and his situation. She was very pleased to hear of the good work done in Tierra de Los Hombres and was especially happy to learn how hard they worked to rehabilitate families and return children to their parents if this was possible. She expressed tremendous admiration for Martine's tenacity and perseverance on David's behalf. Señora Belaunde's support was a further incentive to continue our efforts to secure legal papers for David.

Meanwhile the arrangements for our journey to the Mission at Puerto Ocopa were almost complete. We hoped that our meeting with the padre would finally substantiate the information we had been given at the convent. As far as meeting David's parents was concerned we agreed to act entirely on the advice of the padre.

Although I knew we would be flying directly from Lima to Puerto Ocopa I had not imagined we would be doing so in such a small aeroplane. I do not recall the make of aeroplane, only that it was a small, twin-engined, eight-seater aircraft. I am a white-knuckle flier at the best of times, but when I saw the pilot cramming the luggage compartment – which was the 'nose' compartment of the aircraft – full of heavy camera equipment, I wondered if he really knew what he was doing! I was a little comforted to know that he would be paid only when we were safely returned to Lima. Charlie and Elvira accompanied me to the airport and made light of my nervousness. Later they told me that nothing on earth would have persuaded them to fly in such a tiny aeroplane!

Because Alex wanted to do some filming on the flight, I was put into the seat beside the pilot. Having no desire to be filmed using the little brown paperbag, I tried very hard to quell the flutterings of my stomach! After about twenty minutes of flying-time the pilot explained we were to fly above the mountains and, since the cabin was not pressurised, we would have to use oxygen masks. They were lucky not to have a cardiac arrest on their hands!

After take-off we soon left the dirt and grime of Lima behind and ahead we could see the mountains. We had to fly directly over some of them, and at other times we flew between them. I am not sure which made me more afraid, to be above them or to have them soaring into the sky beside us! In spite of my fears, I could not help admiring the scene around us. The variations of the cloud formations were mesmerising; it was impossible not to be awed by the stark greyness of the towering Andes mountains – they seemed to exude an almost tangible power. Gradually the terrain changed; the contours of the mountains became a little softer, until we were flying over a carpet of lush green vegetation. The pilot pointed out, far below us, the area of grass on which we would land. As we circled the airstrip, lining up for our approach, we could see the mission and the little village very neatly set out alongside it. We could also see a tractor which had just finished trimming the grass on the runway and the pilot told us that the man driving it was Padre Castillo. This was our first glimpse of a man who truly works for, and with, his people.

As we stepped down from the plane we were surrounded by smiling, friendly children. They weren't at all shy and it was obviously not the first time they had seen an aeroplane. We learned that one of the padres from another Mission in the area flew a small supply aircraft to deliver basic necessities. He collected the supplies together in a town named Satipo, and then made the rounds to all the Missions in the area. We were to find out during our stay that fuel for the generator was a major priority. Darkness falls very early in the evening, around five o'clock, and without the generator-powered lights the Mission is in total blackness. On the evening this happened to us there was no moon and the candles we had been advised to take with us came in very handy!

Wishing to disturb Padre Castillo as little as possible until he was finished with his day's work, we quickly introduced ourselves and agreed to meet and talk with him later. The precious daylight hours are never wasted, so the working day begins early and finishes at sundown. Although the Mission buildings are very adequately constructed with proper washing and toilet facilities, there is no water laid on. The village well is no longer in working order, so all water has to be carried from the river. The walk is probably about four or five hundred yards, but with a large heavy container of water on one's head that is a considerable distance! Five o'clock in the morning is not, as we thought it might be, a quiet time to go down to the river to wash. It turned out that everyone goes then; it proved to be a good time to get to know most of the village population and to become known to them.

Because of a sudden change in the weather over the mountains the other half of our group was stranded in Satipo. We had to wait until the following day before we could record interviews with the padre. We were given bedrooms in the newest part of the Mission. The rooms were plain, containing only beds. It was very hot in the wooden building, the windows were small but fortunately were open and covered with mosquito-netting. On the first evening I shared a room with Rita because her husband, who arranged our air travel, was stranded with the other group. Desmond, Alex, Andrew and Colin shared a room and were joined the following night by Kenny and Roy. One could only assume from the remarks made next morning that it was as well Roy did not record the nocturnal noises! After the second detachment arrived, Jan and I shared a room at the rear of the stone chapel building. There were two large windows, neither of which was covered by netting. As I mentioned, it was very dark and when I remarked to the padre how strange it was to have so many birds flying madly around close to the building, he informed us that they were not birds but vampire bats! It took us almost an hour, with Roy's help, to barricade the windows with cardboard and blankets. It was incredibly hot and Jan and I spent the greater part of the night dozing fitfully in between bouts of leaping up because we thought we heard footsteps on the stone stairs or bats flapping around inside the room. In the light of day we were able to laugh at ourselves!

The atmosphere of the Mission is one of friendliness and orderliness. All the tasks, the carrying of water from the river, the gathering together in the church for Mass and the marshalling of the children into classes for school, take place with the minimum of fuss. We had taken a lot of food with us, as this seemed to be the best way in which we could show our appreciation to the padre and the Sisters for giving us some of their precious time.

As I walked around the village I was impressed by its geometric precision. Each group of houses was set out in a square formation and the avenues between the squares each had its own signpost with the name neatly printed on it. Children never take long to get over any shyness they might have, and it is then easier to communicate through them with the adults. Alex and Desmond had taken Polaroid cameras with them; they photographed the children and it was marvellous to watch the hilarity and happiness derived from these instant pictures. Around the village I could see all the usual household activities being taken care of. Washing was being hung neatly on a line; mats were being shaken and floors swept; a child who had hurt his knee while playing was being cuddled and babies were being fed. It is so beautiful there that I couldn't help thinking that these people were the lucky ones.

Many who flocked to Lima and other cities from these areas after the agrarian reform of around 1968 did not find the food, shelter, and work they were looking for, and were faced instead with deprivation and starvation. The ones who stayed behind lead a simple, primitive life, but they are in their own beautiful surroundings, not being forced to live in slums like the *barriada* and beg for a living. Unfortunately the number of people which can be supported in jungle areas is limited. Even with the depopulation caused by the urban drift it is becoming more difficult to extract a living from the land, and without help there is serious concern that many will slowly die of starvation. The principal concept of agrarian reform was that of taking the land from the rich and giving it to the poor, thus providing good fertile land which would be capable of supporting the local population. What happened was that without wages, direction, and the knowledge needed to farm the land, the people became unproductive, desperate, and finally left to search for work elsewhere. It is sad to see acre upon acre of once-fertile land lying empty and going to waste, while people starve.

The exact date of the founding of the Mission at Puerto Ocopa is not known. It was destroyed by an earthquake in 1937 and was reconstructed by Padre Jesus Coicochea in 1947. The Sisters are Franciscan nuns from the Order of the Immaculate Conception and are sent there by appointment.

We spent some time in the classroom with Flori, the young woman who teaches the children of elementary-school age. The schoolroom was neat and tidy and we were very impressed at how hard the children worked. It wasn't just a 'show' for us because we also saw their workbooks which were most impressive. Before school began we were amused to see some of the little girls, with large brooms made from branches tied on to poles, sweeping the entrance clean. Some gourds were hanging on the branches of one of the trees directly outside the classroom and they were filled with beautiful small flowering plants. Flori told us how much the children loved to make these. The atmosphere was light and happy, but there was obviously enough firmness in the guidance of the teacher to get the work done. Padre Castillo teaches the older children and one realises in his classroom there is no time for planting flowers in gourds – advancing years bring responsibility and an increasing workload. It was marvellous – there we were hundreds of miles into the Amazon jungle and those classrooms were as orderly as any I have ever seen. The seriousness with which these young pupils sang their hymn and then got down to the business of lessons in a quiet and orderly fashion was most uplifting!

Padre Teodorico Castillo Coralles was born in 1925 in the department of Arequipa, in a town called Llanahuara. In 1940 he went to the convent in Arequipa and his years of high school study were completed there. He began his noviciado in Lima and continued in the Convento de Ocopa, in Huancayo. He took his solemn vows in 1948 and became a priest in April of 1951. He worked in the Sierra for some time and thereafter went to Puerto Ocopa. When he learned that I am from Scotland he told me he only knew two things about that country. One was whisky, and the other the gardens at Poolewe in the north-west Highlands!

We were in the company of Padre Castillo for only a short time but this was enough to know that he is a man whose work is truly his life, and whose life is his work. He not only works for his people, he works with them. He spends a lot of time out-of-doors and is physically strong. His strength of purpose is very obvious. I am sure that if need be he can be stern, but he is a quiet and gentle man. In addition, the sincerity and enthusiasm he brings to his work give him a unique charisma. He is as impressive sitting on his tractor, or working in the classroom, as he is when conducting Mass. In his little whitewashed chapel in the Peruvian jungle is found an atmosphere of peace and serenity.

When we sat down to talk I expressed my concern as to whether we should attempt to search out the truth about David's parents and background. Padre Castillo had no hesitation at all in advising me that it was right, and good to do so. He had not been at the Mission when David was brought there by his father, and the padre who was there at that time has since died. Taking part in our discussion was the teacher Flori. She had been there when David's father arrived with his sick baby, and remembered clearly how horrified the Sisters were when they first saw the little one. The greater part of David's face was black, he was very thin and obviously far from well.

Flori did not know exactly how the father and son had managed to get to the Mission. She told us that when one of the Sisters attempted to clean the baby's face 'it fell off'. Nothing could have been done for him at the Mission. The Sisters had never before seen a child who had lost so much flesh and they had no idea what to do. The padre arranged to accompany both David and his father to Lima, and the journey took place in July of 1975.

Padre Castillo now took up the story; he told us how, much later, David's parents had been informed that not only had their baby son survived, but he had been taken to Scotland by a surgeon who was taking care of him both in his home and in the hospital. This exciting information was relayed through the regular radio contact between the convent in Lima and the Mission in Puerto Ocopa. When the padre had been told several weeks beforehand that we were searching for more details of David's past, and that we might come to Puerto Ocopa to talk to him, he sent word to David's parents. He said they wanted to meet me and hear as much as possible about David. The padre has worked among these Campa Indians for a long time, therefore who better to advise us than he? He declared that there was no doubt in his mind he should take me to meet them. Together we would find the truth about David.

Padre Castillo made arrangements for us to leave very early the following morning since the journey would take several hours. That evening, however, during his radio contact with Lima, the padre was told to expect an early-morning visit from some army personnel. Apparently, because of the mounting terrorist activity in Peru, all of the Missions and the populated areas around them were being fairly regularly inspected. This was unfortunate since our schedule was such that it was not possible to stay another day. Late in the morning of the following day, however, when the expected visitors had not arrived, Padre Castillo surmised that the visit had been cancelled. If we were to accomplish our mission at all we must leave immediately.

We set off in brilliant sunshine; the heat was quite intense and it was very humid. I have never seen such a strong, swift current and consequently although we were travelling in a long, dug-out canoe with an outboard motor it did not seem to afford much protection between us and the river. In spite of having the motor and the benefit of the current, our journey was expected to take us three hours. I sat in the centre of the canoe beside Padre Castillo and struggled to converse with him in my very poor Spanish; I think his struggles to understand me were greater than mine to speak! He complimented me on being wise enough to wear a large sunhat and laughed when I told him that it was the wisdom of my friends, the Navarros; the hat was Elvira's! I still have the hat, as Elvira gave it to me to keep as a memento of my trip. The padre's hat is, in his own words, 'único'. The fabric is very closely woven, by hand, I believe – like sacking but firmer. It is very big and flops down over his face and neck, giving him complete protection from the sun. It seems to be impervious to sun and rain, both of which it receives in liberal amounts! My linguistic struggles kept my mind off the swishing waters around me and the impending meeting ahead of me.

We were travelling along the River Perené towards the junction between it and the River Ene. These two rivers flow together to form the River Tambo. We knew that Shima, the place where David was born, lay on the River Tambo. Several times as we approached our destination Desmond asked me if I could tell him what I was feeling. I couldn't. As far as thinking about David or his parents was concerned, I was numb. It was as though I was a spectator at this drama. I was aware of the beauty of our surroundings – it was rather like being in the middle of a *National Geographic* photograph. I will probably never see anything more magnificent – the mountains, the shimmering of the water and the trees caused by the heat, the sand and beautiful stones on the shores of the river – and I felt nothing. I think it was because I did not want my dread of losing David to come to the surface. I was not afraid any longer that we were wrong to come. I was sure that Padre Castillo would never have allowed a meeting to take place if it would cause any upset to anyone. I was afraid that when David's parents learned what a great little boy he is and saw from my photographs how well he is progressing, they would want to have him back with them. This feeling became stronger as our journey progressed.

When we arrived, Padre Castillo left us on the shore and he went alone to the village. He came back accompanied by two young boys of about twelve or thirteen years of age, obviously very anxious to have a look at us! The padre told us that David's family had moved to another village further down the river and so we set off again. We had been going for a little over half an hour when above the brush on the steep bank of the river, we saw the roofs of some houses. The padre indicated to our guide that he should pull in and beach the canoe just below the houses. It was very hot, the stones on the shore were burning to the touch. Once again we waited as the padre approached the village. This time he came back alone. He told us that we were welcome to go up to the houses and shelter from the sun, while he went a little further into the jungle to look for David's father who was apparently busy cutting wood.

The first house we came to after climbing the hill was completely enclosed, but as we drew nearer we realised that the walls were not solid but made of woven grasses. This is extremely practical because it allows the passage of both light and air. On one side, the thatched roof extended outwards and was supported at the corners with poles – rather like a carport. There were benches under this shelter and although we did not need to sit down after our long journey in the canoe, we were very happy to be out of the sun. There were few people around and we presumed most villagers would be working while it was still light. Across the little compound I saw a group of women sitting in the shade of an enormous tree, and one of them had a very new baby on her lap. I can never resist looking at small babies; besides I needed something to distract my troubled thoughts, and so I approached them and asked to see the baby. The young mother was just as happy to show her offspring to me as I was to admire him. I had only been with them a few moments when we heard the padre return.

He came into the compound accompanied by several Indians and introduced them to us as David's father, mother, brothers and sisters. I suppose I should have been nervous, but I wasn't. Everything seemed to happen too quickly. The padre introduced us and David's father told us the names of his children. David is the seventh child, and at the time we were there he had eight brothers and sisters but it was obvious that another one would arrive soon.

Finally, from David's father we learned the truth. David was born on 26 December 1974. His father said he was a fine healthy baby with no birth defects. When he was approximately three months old he was bitten by a sandfly. This is not an uncommon event in this part of the world, however; when a sandfly bites the face of a small baby the consequences can be disastrous. Very soon after the bite, said his father, David became sick with a fever, which despite treatment with paste made from herbs became steadily worse.

This seemed to fit the classic description of leishmaniasis – a disease which is prevalent in Central and South America, particularly Brazil and Peru – and is commonly carried by sandflies. The bite may show as only a tiny mark, but extensive destruction of soft tissue and bone may be occurring inside the nose and mouth. Several days or even weeks can elapse before the damage becomes obvious.

When the parents realised that they could do no more to help their child, David's father took him and started what must have been a very lonely and harzardous journey by canoe. I have already mentioned the ferocity of the river's current. Our journey back up-river to the Mission, against the current, took almost five hours; his must have taken much longer – alone with the baby in a canoe which had no engine.

David's mother was very quiet while her husband was speaking but occasionally when he turned to her for confirmation she nodded. She did not smile, and I wondered what she thought as we all stood there listening. How different I must have seemed to her! I wondered if she could accept that I loved her little boy as much as any mother could. Since each statement had to be translated and relayed back and forth through our interpreter, the story took some time. It was so important that we clearly understood exactly what David's father was telling us. So intent were we in listening, it was not until David's father had come to the end of his tale that I realised how many other villagers had gathered around us and were listening too. We asked David's father if he would like to see photographs of David and he very enthusiastically said he would. It was fascinating to see his reaction. I could not understand every word he said but it was easy to see, by the movement of his hands and the excitement in his voice as he showed them to his wife and family, that he was pleased. For the first time, David's mother smiled as she looked at the photograph of David.

There was great excitement as the photographs were passed around and the other villagers questioned David's parents. They probably had not known anything of the baby since the family had so recently moved into this vicinity. At this point all my fears came flooding back. It was a bitter-sweet moment to see those people so happy about their son – because in my heart he was our son. I asked Padre Castillo to explain to David's father that, although I was happy to be able to tell them of his recovery and progress, I needed to know whether or not they wanted to have him back. Padre Castillo put my question to David's father. He also explained that, although I did not want to think of losing him, I understood the decision must be theirs; further, that although David was well and had made a lot of progress, the reconstruction was by no means finished. For me, this was a moment of awful apprehension: would they want him back? Could I accept it if they did? David's father turned to me; speaking slowly and clearly so that I would understand, he said, 'He is no longer Campa and cannot be again.' He said that David would not be well accepted in his own country. He asked me to tell Ian how he admired his skill, he was proud for David to be with him, and he wished us joy. It was a serious and moving speech. I told him, in return, that he should be very glad that his effort to save his baby's life had been successful because his son had grown into a courageous and happy boy, of whom they could be very proud. With this approval from David's father, we had advanced yet another step towards making David a legal member of our family.

In answer to Padre Castillo's request for details, David's father told us the exact date of David's birth and he explained that normally he would have gone to the Mission to record the birth within four or five months. It was because the baby became sick so quickly that he did not do this. He also said that the baptism had been properly registered at the Mission before the baby was taken to Lima. He went on to relate how they had been told of David going to a foreign country for treatment, and being cared for by the surgeon and his family. At that time he made a declaration giving up all rights to his son and wished him happiness. He said that this declaration was also formally recorded at the Mission. The padre made a careful note of this, and then suddenly it was time to leave. We seemed to have been there such a short time yet we had achieved so much. All that was left was to say goodbye. As I shook hands with David's mother she asked me directly, 'When can I see him again?' Rita's voice quavered as she translated this for me. She suddenly had a lump in her throat and so did I. How well we could understand her feelings of sadness and curiosity about the young son she might never see again! I gently told her that perhaps he would return when he was a bigger boy.

As we walked down the hill towards the river I turned to look back and I will always remember the scene as David's family stood there together, watching us leave, with the little village and the jungle forming a dramatic backdrop. Padre Castillo told me that he wanted me, my husband, my family, and all the other people who had helped David to know what a good thing we had done. He is truly a man of understanding and compassion. He realised how uncertain I had been of the right or wrong of our actions; he understood also my fear of losing David. His assurance that to meet David's parents could only bring happiness was right. They now know for certain that David is well and happy. We, in turn, can tell David about the people who gave birth to him and how proud he should be that they cared enough to give him up.

We were a quiet group as we set off on our journey back to the Mission, each busy with his own thoughts. Gone was my numbness of a few hours ago, instead I felt relieved; glad that we had brought happiness instead of distress but also sad for the family trying to imagine David in his new surroundings. How much I hoped they believed and trusted in our love for David! As all these emotions flooded in, I was suddenly exhausted.

Now we were battling against the current of the river and in spite of the motor we added two hours to the travelling time. We had been witness to the beauty of a sunlit panorama of sky, mountains, river, and jungle vegetation on the way out and now we were privileged to experience one of the most magnificent sunsets I have ever seen. The weather, however, is not always kind and as we sat quietly watching the sun go down and listening to the sound of the river rushing by, we were treated to yet another aspect of weather in the jungle regions of the Andes – rain! Not a gentle Scottish mist, or even the kind of steady downpour so common in Glasgow, but a deluge of water which soaked us in seconds and which continued for more than half an hour. At one point the engine of the outboard motor coughed and stopped. There were a few anxious moments when we were at the mercy of the current until our guide, who thankfully was experienced, uncovered a second motor. By the time we finally got back to the Mission it was very dark and we had dried out.

Padre Castillo remained awake for the greater part of that night, searching through the carefully kept and beautifully written records of births, marriages, and deaths, in the Mission. He found the record of David's baptism, which took place on 29 July 1975. He also found the document, dated November 1977, stating that David's father, knowing that he did not have the means to make his son well again, and that he had gone to live with a foreign family, surrendered all rights to him and wished him much happiness. All the BBC team were happy to witness Padre Castillo hand over these precious documents to me. It was a time full of hope; finally we might have success in adopting David. Another important step had been taken, although as yet I still did not have an actual birth certificate.

There was one more very touching moment to experience before we left to return to Lima. As all the equipment was being loaded into the plane, Flori came to say goodbye to me. With her was Eduardo, a little boy who had become like a shadow to us during our stay at the Mission. Flori told us he was three years old, his mother had died in childbirth, and he now lived with her. Even as we walked towards the aeroplane Flori was hurriedly writing a letter. She asked me to give it to David. An approximate translation of the letter is as follows:

David – your mother came here to Puerto and brought much emotion, because she brought to us good news of the progress of your health. I am Floripes Ruiz del Aguila – they call me Flori. I saw your photographs and I am particularly happy to see how handsome you are becoming. Study well, David. Here we remember you and we pray that you will become as good a man as the parents whom you are happy to live with. You will see a photo of little Eduardo. He is an orphan because his mother died when he was born. I have taken charge of him and I love him very much. He is three years old. He is very mischievous and loves to dance; he likes also to go to school with his little friends. David, the plane is here and I say goodbye with much love. A big hug for you and also for your brother and sisters whom I saw in the photographs.

Goodbye, David. Flori Ruiz del Aguila.

I feel extremely privileged to have come to know Padre Castillo, a truly good man whose total concern and effort is for others. I am grateful that I can now assure David of the effort his father made to get help for him. I hope that when he is a young man he will be proud of his father for undertaking the journey which made his survival possible.

Our own journey had been brought about by the concern Desmond and Alex had for David as they worked with him and grew to know him. Indeed, for the whole team he had become more than just the subject of their documentary. They were anxious to help him in any way they could, for his future as much as his present. As a family we would like to express our appreciation of the BBC who financed the journey, which Ian and I could never have done by ourselves.

We left Peru, having accomplished a great deal, confident that the papers we now possessed and the promise of help from the President's wife, would lead to our eventual adoption of David.

After the filming was complete, there was still quite a bit of work to be done in selecting and editing the film for the screen. The programmes were shown in the UK on two successive nights in August 1983. By and large the critics were unanimous in their agreement that the programmes were well-constructed and sensitive work. There were, as always, minor criticisms, but what concerned us was that the problems had been shown honestly and clearly. We thought they had been. No matter how clearly or how forcefully one might set forth a subject, people will only see what they open their hearts and minds to. For some people it was probably just an interesting story which they hoped would eventually have a happy ending, but others understood the underlying message.

We received literally hundreds of letters from people who were moved by what they had seen. Some wrote to say how grateful they were for being allowed to witness the rebuilding of David's face, and were fascinated by the amazing developments in the field of plastic surgery. Others reacted to the courage and perseverance of a little boy who had withstood so much and faced so much more. The effect of this made them look at their own attitudes to much more minor mishaps like the weather, a headache, or any of the thousand and one things we all tend to complain about. Some of the letters were very moving. Several wrote to say that they had been helped by the way in which we dealt with David's problems and now felt that what they were facing was not nearly so bad by comparison. Ian and I have since written to all of these people and have told them of the tremendous help we have been given, just simply from reading about their circumstances and how they deal with them. A few people wrote of their need for help with children suffering from various forms of facial deformity and Ian was able to advise them of surgeons in Britain who might be able to assist them.

Knowing how others have dealt with similar problems has not only been helpful in my everyday life with a handicapped child, but has also been stimulating and humbling. So many people facing circumstances which, for most of us, might seem hopeless, wrote with such a lively sense of humour and lack of self-pity that we are truly in admiration of them. They strengthen my resolve to become a better person. I was comforted also, and perhaps my burden of guilt and shame lessened a little, when I realised that other mothers had thoughts like those I have had. They too have said to themselves – 'If only I had never seen him', or 'Why me – why my son?' This feeling comes with fatigue and frustration when we think that perhaps we have not done as well as we could. Almost as soon as it has been given substance, reason takes over and we know very well that the answer to our pathetic question is 'Why not – who would you choose to carry the load instead?' We don't really mean those things and it takes only a moment for feelings of humility and thankfulness to come flooding in. We are privileged to have the opportunity to love and raise these children, and perhaps more importantly, to be loved by them. Nothing gives me a warmer feeling than when, after I have tucked David in bed for the night and given him his goodnight kiss, he says, 'Goodnight, Mum, see you in the morning.' I realise how lucky I am, in spite of all the frustrations and fatigue, to have our five children.

One aspect in the upbringing of a handicapped child which can be very difficult is that of discipline. It is important for the handicapped child to be taught behaviour which is socially acceptable. If a child is to be accepted by society, then he or she must learn to live by its rules. It is not until one faces the problems of bringing up children that the reality of how difficult this can be, becomes apparent. I can remember, before Ian and I had a family of our own, criticising some badly-behaved children and vowing that we would never have children like that! Our rather smug attitude vanished rapidly when we realised that each child is so much of an individual that trying to teach five of them the same ground rules can mean five different experiences for the parent. Children are expert at exerting moral blackmail to achieve their own ends. We have very frequently been told by each of our children that they are the 'only ones' not allowed to do this, that, or the other. It is sometimes difficult to harden one's resolve against this kind of thing but when the handicapped child resorts to blackmail then it is even more of a problem. It is essential to maintain consistent standards. I have been told of a child confined to a wheelchair, who, when she was being reprimanded by her mother, said, 'How can you treat a cripple like this?' That really hurts, and no one knows it better than the child. If children are allowed to manipulate people and situations at home, they find it impossible to deal with outside situations where this kind of behaviour is unacceptable.

All children get a little spoiling when they are sick or hurt. This is what makes it so much more difficult to be firm with David than it was with his brother and sisters. There are so many occasions when, because of surgery, he has a lot of pain and is not feeling well. Worse than the physical pain is the mental agony of looking in the mirror and knowing that what you see is not only much worse than it was before, but is even grotesque. When, for reconstructive purposes, tissue is transferred from one part of the body to another, much more has to be moved than is necessary. When a period of settling has taken place the tissue is then contoured and trimmed. These are very difficult times for David. His expectations have been dashed and he has to accept that his appearance is worse than before; although it is sad to see his disappointment, it is also uplifting to see his struggle to overcome this and look forward to the next time. He tries to laugh at his own appearance but sometimes the laughter quickly turns to tears. One time he said to me, 'Don't tell Dad we cried, Mum, he did his best.'

David has absolute faith in anything Ian does for him. Whenever he sees another child with a facial deformity he says, 'I bet Dad could help that boy.' Little boys always put their dads on pedestals and endow them with Superman qualities – this of course makes a dad feel great, but when something looks as if it might go wrong and David says, 'It's OK. Dad will fix it', it is very touching but puts an enormous strain on Ian. David sometimes teases Ian and pretends that he does not like what has been done. Ian, in turn, has then to pretend to be upset, whereupon David says, 'I'm only joking, Dad!' His wonderful gurgling laugh will then come bubbling out and Ian comes in for a bit of kidding. Our own children have learned from their little brother that pride in personal appearance, when it is to do with being beautiful or handsome, is a stupid thing. They have seen how people turn away from David without even giving him a chance to show that he is just as normal as they are. Through the pain of David's hurt, they have learned to be very careful about rejecting someone just because they look different.

XI
DAVID TODAY

The David of today bears little resemblance to the small boy I met at Glasgow airport in February 1977. At that time he was tiny, pathetically ugly, very cold and very afraid. In eight years, he has grown considerably and at the age of ten years he is of average height: four feet and three inches tall. Within the areas of society in which he feels safe and unthreatened – home, school, church and activities related to these – he is an outgoing, friendly boy with a really lively sense of humour. Anything he gets involved in he does with enthusiasm. He is a superb little athlete and is very happy participating in athletics, gymnastics, and sport in general. His true love is football, or soccer as it is known in the United States. Last season he was captain of his team and Fred Regal, the coach, assured me that he was chosen absolutely on merit. Fred also told me that there were times when he held his breath and prayed when he saw David going in to tackle in his own inimitably enthusiastic and fearless fashion. The team also contained two little Vietnamese boys so David was not the only small black-haired, brown-eyed boy scurrying around. Although doing well and winning are important to all participants in games, we are happy that David does not base his enthusiasm on always winning or being best. He is as disappointed as anyone else when he loses but he doesn't give up. He is an excellent swimmer and is a member of the Rochester swimming club. When he competes in minor swim meets he gets into the water and gives it all he's got! Times do not seem to be important to him, he never goes rushing off to see what his time is so that he can boast about it. His natural ability in the gym makes him a popular fellow to have on the team if games are being played, but he is also aware of the skill and effort other children put into their playing and he cheers on his team-mates with great gusto!

He is a kind little boy and I think the many talks we have had about the unhappiness his own deformity has brought him have helped him to be more aware of the feelings of others who have some disability or who, for other reasons, are unhappy. As a family, we have learned to understand that some people are disagreeable because of unhappiness in their own lives. It is therefore better to appreciate all the times when people show their friendship by caring and by their supportive attitudes, rather than dwelling on unpleasant experiences.

Lest you think after all this that he is a paragon of virtue, let me assure you he is not! He can be fiery-tempered, stubborn, huffy, obstructive and sneaky, but since I have experienced all of these characteristics in his brother and sisters I take them to be reassuring signs that he is normal! After being really naughty he can, with a look of total innocence on his face, deny all knowledge of the particular incident being discussed. Although from day to day all the usual name-calling, skirmishing, and sibling rivalry goes on, particularly between Andrew and David, the girls and Andrew are still as protective of David as they ever were and he always speaks of them with pride. The spontaneous bursts of gurgling laughter with which he reacts to situations which seem funny to him can very quickly reduce us all to tears of laughter!

At home he loves it when we play games together – he likes any of the usual board games – Monopoly, Cluedo, Risk and so on. He is helpful around the house and he loves to help his dad in the garden. He is always excited when Linda and Susan come home from university. He enjoys mealtimes so much when the whole family is around the kitchen table. When we are all together, Ian will often conduct little quizzes – capital cities of the world, or famous quotations – or we play 'I spy', guessing only objects which are on the table. Discussions often become heated and David views this with great amusement. His eyes fairly dance when he says to me, 'I'll argue with Dad too, Mum – when I'm bigger!'

David has completed more than two full school years in Rochester and he has settled very well indeed. He is totally accepted and well liked. It is always hard for him in any new situation. Understandably he is wary and very conscious of people's reaction to him initially. Prior to him beginning school I went to speak to the headmaster and the teachers of the first four grades. They were all in complete agreement with our wish that David be treated as a normal child with no special privileges because of his appearance. I did ask that a simple explanation be given to the children of why David looks the way he does. The result of this was to dismiss curiosity and reassure the very young children. It did not take long before David's classmates realised that he was just another 'new boy' and the differences in his appearance and speech – due mainly to his Scottish accent – were soon accepted and forgotten.

When David is eating, the lack of teeth in his upper jaw gives his face a kind of squishy look, rather like those soft foam-rubber toy faces which you can distort in all manner of ways. This aspect of his appearance made children reluctant to sit beside him in the school dining-room. This caused him quite a bit of unhappiness, but the phase passed as the children got to know him better. He became much happier and altogether more relaxed about going to school. I think it would be difficult to find a situation in which he could be more comfortable. His teacher has encouraged open discussion in the classroom in which the other children have been able to learn in a straightforward, unemotional atmosphere the frightening aspects of being someone with a facial deformity. David, in turn, has learned to accept that the curiosity people display about his appearance is, many times, a concerned desire to know the cause rather than just thoughtless curiosity. Seeing how the children benefit from those candid, factual conversations reinforces my belief that we must be able to bring our attitudes and concerns about deformity and handicap out into the open if we want to progress.

We still have our quiet times, David and I. After surgery when he is not attending school, he and I are alone most of the day; we talk about how far he has progressed surgically and how he now feels about himself. We have had some difficult situations to face recently but by talking about our fears and hopes I think David has managed to stay on a fairly level emotional plane. First of all there was all the excitement of facing the major surgery which gave him the first real hope of having teeth. Very soon after, having got through that, we had to face the undeniable fact that David's facial bone, which has all come from different parts of his body, is not yet ready to take foreign material. For Ian's sake he tried to be very brave about having to go back to the operating room. He made two more visits there before everything was cleared up. This protective instinct of the child for the parent is really most amazing and, from my discussions with other parents, I know that children even younger than David try to hide their unhappiness. Although, as I have said, I try not to over-protect David, I do watch carefully for any signs that he is trying to cover up a situation which is causing him distress. It is good that David can be happy with what has been achieved, but for Ian, at the moment, the prospect is bleak. He feels that we have taken several steps backward and he is unsure of how that lost ground might be regained. At times like these it is very difficult for him to be the objective surgeon rather than the despairing dad! Everything that was done for David was done with the best of intentions and everyone involved hoped that this procedure would be a momentous step forward. It was not to be, and so we go on again, building him up until the time is right to retrieve what has been lost.

Throughout the years we have been in America our efforts to achieve a legal adoption for David have continued. With the help of the Navarros, we have retained lawyers who, although hopeful in the beginning, were never able to have the papers presented in court. On several occasions, Ian and I submitted to being fingerprinted; we have been investigated by Rochester Police, FBI and Interpol. Our home has been inspected by social workers and photographs of the kitchen, living-room and David's bedroom submitted. Several certificates have also been presented – from our bank concerning our financial standing; from the Mayo Clinic declaring Ian to be honourable, a surgeon of international repute and an asset to the community; of residency; of health and birth and marriage – but there has still been no progress through court. We had been told that the biggest stumbling block was that, by Peruvian law, adoptive parents had to be fifty years of age and must have no children. By those terms we certainly were not eligible – and although, as time passed, we came closer to qualifying as far as age was concerned, we were always going to have our children. It seemed to us that it must surely be possible for David's case to be treated as 'special' but we never made any progress. Señora Belaunde's promise to help could only be implemented once the documents were actually presented at a court hearing. We were determined to plod on, but there were many times when I was very discouraged.

Another offer of help was, however, forthcoming from a totally unexpected source. Cardinal Landazuri Ricketts, Primate of Peru, visited Rochester in 1982 on a visit to the Mayo Clinic for his annual medical check-up. He heard that Ian was both father and surgeon to a Peruvian Indian boy and asked to meet us. At that time he also met David. When he learned of what we were doing for David and how little progress we had made towards adoption, his reaction was that he was ashamed to be Peruvian. On hearing that Ian and I were to be in Lima shortly after, he invited us to meet him there so that he could try to help us. While we were in Peru he gave us the services of the lawyer in the Archbishop's Palace and that gentleman took possession of our documents and gave us great hope that he, endorsed by Cardinal Landazuri, could finally achieve adoption. This, however, was not to be. The lawyer was not the upright man he appeared to be. We thought work was in progress, but more than six months later he had to be asked to leave the services of the Cardinal. It was with great regret that the Cardinal then wrote to us, saying that 'Due to bureaucracy he would no longer be able to help us'. We were once again in limbo.

During the time David was recovering from the initial surgery we were told that a shortened version of the BBC documentary was to be shown on NBC television in the United States. The programme had already won first place in an international documentary competition in New York in 1983, a fitting tribute to the skill with which Alex McCall directed and Desmond Wilcox produced. At this time David still knew nothing about his parents. He has always known that he came from Peru and that he was not born to us as Linda, Susan, Sarah and Andrew were. He has also always been aware that his skin is darker than ours and that he is a Peruvian Indian. Although he has known several children who are adopted and he knows that we are fighting for the 'magic piece of paper' which will make him 'legal', he has never asked for any information about his family in Peru. I believe that fear of the unknown has a little to do with this, together with a subconscious desire to maintain the status quo and to keep buried all his earlier insecurities. Now, with the national television showing of the film, David had to be told the truth. He had to be helped to feel proud of the people who gave birth to him. Without this knowledge he could have been hurt by unthinking comments from other children at school about his obviously primitive and very poor parents. This we very definitely wanted to avoid. He had to be told the whole story, but how were we to do this?

Since my meeting with David's parents in the Peruvian jungle, I had often wondered when and how to tell him his own story simply and honestly without any drama. It is strange how sometimes by a small quirk of fate life presents us with an undreamt-of opportunity. I mentioned in the last chapter that we received many letters after the showing of the documentary in Britain. One of those letters gave me what seemed to be the perfect opening to tell David of his parents, brothers and sisters, in faraway Peru.

David had received a very touching letter from a little boy in England called Ben. Ben had seen part of the documentary on television and was immediately aware of several similarities between himself and David. He is adopted and he wrote, 'My earth mummy is English and my earth daddy is Scottish like yours.' He went on to tell

David that his 'heaven' mother and father were Filipina Bontoc Indian and Filipino Chinese, respectively. He told David of the things he liked to do, and about his cat, dog and rabbit. He was also happy to notice that David has skin the same colour as his own. He and David have since corresponded and I hope that they will continue to do so as they grow older. Perhaps some day they may meet!

One day after David's surgery, before he was allowed to walk about, he and I were sitting quietly together playing cards when the thought came to me that a good way to introduce David to the story of his early life would be through Ben's letter. We talked about Ben and their letters to each other and I asked David if he remembered what Ben had told him about being adopted and about his parents who were now dead. David said he did remember.

'David, do you ever think about your real parents in Peru?' I asked him.

Without faltering in his dealing of the cards and without any change of expression he replied, 'No.'

I really did not know whether to laugh or cry – but there could be no turning back now. I went on to tell him about my journey far into the jungle and my meeting with his mother and father, brothers and sisters. He listened quietly, and after a slight pause asked me, 'Are you going to send me back now, Mum?' In that moment, his voice and his eyes told me that all his old fear and insecurity had returned. I quickly assured him that we could never send him back because he was our son now, even without the 'magic piece of paper'. After a little more thought he asked, 'Did they not want me because I look like this?' How my heart went out to him! On one hand he needed to be reassured of his place with us, but on the other hand was the hurt of not being wanted by his family in Peru. After we had talked for a long time and I had shown him all the photographs I had brought back, he understood that his parents had loved him so much that they had given him up to enable him to have the opportunity to survive and be happy. After a little while he became less serious and when Sarah and Andrew came home from school he joked with them about the large number of brothers and sisters he now had!

To prepare him further for the NBC programme we showed David the full documentaries as they had been presented in Britain. His comment about them was: 'It's all a bit boring, isn't it, Dad – all that talking!' He was excited to see Mary and Robert on film and to see himself with Sally, their dog. He liked the part when he played in the park in Glasgow with Jane and Philip, and in Spain when he talked in the boat with Desmond. He carefully watched the scenes concerning his family in the jungle but it was obvious that he does not really associate himself with that way of life. His schoolteacher was extremely helpful and supportive in helping David to discuss the whole course of events with his classmates both before and after the American screening. David knows that they care, and he has been able to help them by answering their questions. When he was in hospital the children all made cards and wrote wonderfully encouraging messages in them. They made up games and puzzles for him so that he would not be bored. They bought him a beautiful stuffed dog; he called it 'Lucky' because we had talked about how lucky he was to have such caring friends at school. The television programme was also discussed as a class project and thus everything was kept on a very even keel. The result of this has been to give him a greater sense of security than ever.

In Sunday school David is also accepted for what he is and not for how he looks. His teachers tell me he contributes openly in discussion without embarrassment. During the time he was absent after surgery his classmates were asked to make clothes-peg 'Jesus' figures to illustrate the Bible lessons they had been studying. David's teacher came to visit him and gave him the material for his figure and said that if he felt well enough he should do it and we could send it along the following Sunday. Since he had plenty of time on his hands David was able to exercise a lot of care when he was making his figure and apparently the children in his class were impressed with the long white beard he had given his 'Moses'!

As David has grown, so has his awareness of the problems encountered by someone with a facial deformity. He fully realises that there are other children who have to bear that particular cross. We keep in touch with many of the children he has got to know through his father's work and he takes a great interest in how they are progressing. He looks forward to seeing them in the summer when they all come back for surgery. Jeremy McIntyre is one of the children who is most often in hospital at the same time as David. I have come to know Jeremy's parents well and their warmth, common sense, and friendliness has been of great comfort to me. I remember well the first time David and I met Jeremy. The two boys were to be sharing a room in St Mary's. Jeremy had already been there for two weeks, and he had undergone some major craniofacial surgery. At that point he was well recovered but still had his teeth wired together; because of this it was a little difficult to understand what he was saying. He was delighted to acquire a room-mate and as soon as we entered he began to bombard David with questions as to why he was there, what surgery he was to have and who was his doctor. David, as I have mentioned, is never very happy about being admitted to hospital even if it is only for one night, so he was very quiet. At first he had a little difficulty in understanding Jeremy and I acted as an interpreter. I told Jeremy that on this occasion David was only having a very small operation to make his lip look better. To Jeremy's question about who his surgeon was, David quietly replied, 'Dr Jackson.' This sent Jeremy off into a frenzy of delight and he told David that Dr Jackson was his doctor also and not only that, he had had him before David. I hid a smile and waited to hear what David's reply to this piece of 'one-upmanship' would be. He looked straight at Jeremy and said: 'He's my dad.'

Jeremy was totally disbelieving but when I corroborated David's statement he obviously had to keep up his end of the conversation and told David with great satisfaction, 'But you're only having a little bit done, Dr Jackson took off my head and sewed it back on again!' He leaned forward and parted his hair so that David could see the scar from the incision which extended from above one ear, right across the top of his head to just above the other ear. No question about it, round one went to Jeremy! This was Jeremy's interpretation of the surgery in which the skin of his forehead and face was peeled back and the facial bones rearranged. The competition over, I sat with the boys, one on either side of me, and read to them a little before leaving them to settle down for the night.

David has also had some very special, warm and rewarding experiences with adults who have faced surgery and deformity. Candy Wood is a patient of Ian's who, at the early age of thirty, became aware that she had a particularly bad and life-threatening malignant tumour inside her face and head. She has undergone several major operations, and has not only survived but it seems that the tumour has been completely eradicated. Ian had, literally, to take her face apart to enable him to remove the tumour. She now has a scar running down one side of her nose. This is not very noticeable and can be concealed rather well with a small amount of make-up. She has quite bad distortion of her forehead due to loss of bone and tissue which as yet Ian has not reconstructed. She has also considerable loss of the hair-bearing skin of her scalp. For several months after surgery, while everything was settling down, Candy worked wonders with pretty bright scarves which she wound around her head so that instead of looking as though she was covering something up, in fact, she looked quite 'racy'. Now with the help of a hairpiece she does not need the scarves, and if one had not known her before her surgery it would be very difficult to tell that anything was amiss. Candy's courage, faith and optimism are second to none. She has helped many people by discussing with them her own experiences, fears, and hopes. She has talked to David about how it is to 'look different' and she has shown him the extent of her own deformity. From this David has been helped to learn that, although it is not easy and although there may be many times when one feels really down, it is possible to look outwards and be positive. I admire Candy's courage and her compassion for others more than she will ever know and we appreciate especially the precious time she has given to helping David.

Many people ask if David will go back to live in Peru when he is an adult. We have no way of knowing what the future will bring for David, any more than we know what lies ahead for our other children. I think it is unreasonable and romantic to think that he will be motivated in any way to go back to work among his 'own people'. Who are his own people? He came to us when he was only two years old and he considers himself to be Scottish! His father, a wise man, realises that David is no longer a Campa Indian and will never think of himself as such. How could he? He remembers nothing of his life in Peru and since most of his time was spent in Hospital del Niño there is nothing good for him to remember. I think that it is entirely likely that at some time he will want to go back to Peru to visit and to meet his family but it could be unrealistic to expect that he will want to live there. We will encourage him to work in the Indian communities in the country of his birth if he wishes to, but we will not try to make him feel in any way guilty if he does not. He is a kind and caring person now, and if these fine attributes remain then I am sure that he will, of his own accord, realise the importance of giving assistance in some way to underprivileged countries. Such a desire must come from within David and I have little doubt that it will.

The city of Rochester in Minnesota has become the third most important city in David's life. It is a city which has literally been built in the midst of cornfields! It is not a big city by American standards, the population is approximately sixty thousand. Rochester is best known for its world-famous Mayo Clinic. For countless thousands of people in the United States of America and other countries, the Clinic is a kind of medical Mecca.

William Worral Mayo set up practice in Rochester in 1883. In August of that year a tornado struck the city. In the resulting devastation it was found that there were twenty-six dead and more than thirty people seriously injured. Dr W. W. Mayo set up an emergency clinic in a dance hall in the main street, and was helped in his work by a group of Sisters of St Francis. They had arrived in Rochester several years earlier to found an academy for young women. By 1888 both sons, William and Charles, had joined their father in practice in Rochester. The first official Mayo Clinic, completed in 1914, was a small red-brick building built on the site of Dr W. W. Mayo's home. The original St Mary's Hospital was built by the Sisters of St Francis and was opened for patients on 30 September 1889. It contained forty beds and one operating room. St Mary's today has upwards of one thousand beds and fifty operating rooms. As the Clinic expanded over the years, the need for a large hospital was recognised. St Mary's is situated about half a mile from the Clinic, on Second Street. The new hospital, Rochester Methodist Hospital, sponsored by the Methodist Church, was opened in 1966 and has over eight hundred beds and thirty-eight operating rooms.

Because of the Clinic, Rochester is a city that is familiar with the needs of sick and handicapped people, thus, for the greater part, it is a city that is kind to David. His appearance is met with a candid and concerned interest. As in any place where one settles and makes a home, there are those who become a part of everyday life and who, because of their own particular charisma, endear themselves to one. David is very fond of one such lady who works in the large store in which we do most of our grocery shopping. Emily has become a real friend; she never fails to ask how David is doing and when she sees him she tells him how much he is improving. When he is in hospital or at home after surgery she sends him 'get well' cards. A remark Emily made to me one day caused me to remember some words written by Robert Burns, our Scottish poet. Burns was a man of the people and much of his poetry contained the wisdom of someone who studied and understood the strengths, weaknesses and vanities of his fellow man. One day Emily was commenting on how much better David was looking and she said to me, 'You know, Mrs Jackson, David doesn't look half bad. Before anyone criticises *his* face they should take a look in the mirror!' Robert Burns's sentiments were the same:

> *'O wad some pow'r the giftie gie us*
> *To see oursels as others see us!'*

Perhaps, if more often we looked at ourselves clearly, as through the eyes of others, we might see the truth instead of the flattering image we may carry in our heads! We may see what a mockery pride makes of us and we may then allow a new awareness to guide us as we look at our fellow man.

The most important aspect of David's life, next to his emotional well-being and the physical effects of his surgery, is his education. Ian and I believe that in giving David the very best education possible we will be giving him the greatest chance for happiness and fulfilment in life. In spite of all that David has withstood so far – the initial fear of the unknown, the bewilderment of not understanding the language, the insecurity of not knowing if he was accepted and the pain and suffering of surgery – and in spite of how much he has been helped by people like Candy, he has still to face his own Goliath.

In today's society the teenager is confronted by many pressures and it is hard to hold on to what is good and wholesome. It is hard enough for the youngster who has no disability, let alone one who has first of all had to come to terms with facial deformity. At the present time David is extroverted and out-going and does not wallow in self-pity or look for special treatment. It may be, however, that his friendly personality may make him more vulnerable to some knocks along the way. We pray that the support we give him through just loving him and being there for him at all times, will be a steadying influence. We hope it will help to give him the courage to withstand the hurts and to maintain his sunny character over the years. Linda, Susan, Sarah and Andrew have learned to be very positive in their attitude to anyone who causes David embarrassment or hurt. Without being impolite, they make it very clear that David is not an object of pity and is totally aware of any slight either to his intellect or his appearance. From the very beginning they have shared their lives with David; now they have assured us that, should anything happen to us, their love and protection of him will not fail and they will continue to fight for his right to be one of the family.

It seems that, at long last, I have come to terms with my own struggling emotions. We have tried to make every aspect of David's life as normal as possible, particularly his relationship within the family. I haven't interfered with any of the usual squabbles between brothers and sisters, nor have I tried to shield David from all the problems of integrating and settling in at school. Many children have a tough time at a new school initially and as long as I was sure that there was no direct unpleasantness because of his appearance, I allowed him time to be accepted for what he is. In doing all this, it seems that I have been blinded to my own introspection. I have worried and felt ashamed about having emotions which I thought were wrong. I have been trying so hard to give David what is best, what is right and what is normal, that I have allowed my judgement of my own normal feelings to be abnormally hard. What mother, after all, has not at some time thought longingly of the days before she had children, when she was a person and not just a 'mum'? I never thought that I was particularly wicked, during the very busy years when my own four children were babies, for the many times I sighed for the days of freedom, before children, and, dare I say it, even before husband!

As time has passed and I have talked with other mothers in similar situations, I have been able to come to terms with and accept the fact that it is all right to be angry – angry at myself, angry at the circumstances that brought David to me, angry that this small boy – or any small child – should have to face life with such a burden to bear. It is all right to be sometimes sad, sometimes tired, sometimes even a little bitter; it is all right because it is a part of love. When I have felt it necessary to place restrictions on what the children can or cannot be allowed to do, I have often said to them that it is because we love them. I have seen the look of disbelief on their faces! There are many times when the very fact that love exists is the cause of anger – when someone you love arrives home long after they have been expected and many hours have been spent worrying, do you always rush to them, hug them and welcome them, or do you sometimes become unreasonably and illogically angry and vent all that anger on the loved one? The anger is there because of the love, and I have finally come to know that it is all right to be angry – because after the anger there may even be a firmer and more understanding love.

In spite of all the kind things people have said about us for taking David into our family I still strongly maintain that we are in no way unique or special. David has taught us many things, both as individuals and as a family. I feel privileged that through taking care of David I have met, albeit many times simply through correspondence, many extraordinary, good and strong human beings. Some who are themselves in some way disabled, some who have disabled children, and some who, simply because of their own innate goodness, devote their lives to caring for people less fortunate than themselves. I cannot pay high enough tribute to those people or to anyone who, even just once, steps outside the comfortable routine of their own lives to help another less fortunate.

As a result of the NBC presentation of the documentary, interest was aroused and a number of people wrote to Senator Rudy Boschwitz, Republican senator for Minneapolis and St Paul. They asked him to help us to obtain resident status for David in the United States so that we would no longer have the worry of David being deported if his visa was not renewed. We appreciate the help they are giving in this matter.

We were particularly moved by a letter from Chief Louis F. LaFountain of the Christian Pembina Chippewa Indians. He thought it may be that if David became a member of the Chippewa tribe he would perhaps then have the right to live in the United States with the status of resident alien, which is what we have as a family. This was indeed a most spontaneous and generous gesture by a man whose people have a long and proud heritage. It seems, in fact, that legally David would not benefit from becoming a member of Chief Louis' tribe, since he could only take residency and citizenship if he remained on the reservation. The warmth and caring that this offer signifies, however, is unequalled.

In an age where great improvements have been achieved, making it physically easier for disabled people to lead lives as close to normal as possible, it is essential that our attitudes to these people also improve, in order that all efforts be concerted. Let it become possible for those who, as children, learn to trust and love, to be accepted in adulthood also, for their qualities as individuals. I pray that in our search for a better society we come to know that the indispensable and intrinsic qualities of the nature of man have little to do with his physical appearance. Love is conveyed by the touch of a hand on a fevered brow, whether the hand is rough or smooth. A child feels safe with his hand in the hand of his mother, whether the hand be manicured or coarsened by household tasks. All human beings should be able to feel safe in the knowledge that, regardless of how they appear, they are capable of giving and receiving love.

I hope that those of you who took time seven years ago to listen to the plea for help for a small Peruvian Indian boy with an enormous facial deformity, will feel that you know him now, even just a little. Without your help he could not be the happy, well-adjusted boy that he is. You can be justifiably proud of what you have done. Thank you.

XII
POSTSCRIPT

In Satipo, Junín province, Peru, on 14 November 1984, a document was signed in which David Lopez became David Jackson.

Eleanor Griffis de Zuniga, known to us as Eli, is the Editor of the *Lima Times*. She worked closely with Desmond Wilcox and Alex McCall in 1982 during the making of the documentary *Marjorie's Quest*. Eli became involved with David's story and was horrified to discover how many attempts had been made to adopt David, only to fail. Eli's national pride dictated that something had to be done to put matters right. She retained a lawyer, greatly experienced in matters of adoption, who, having reviewed all our previous attempts, said that the only way left was to take the case to a court in the province in which David was born. It was necessary for the case to proceed in two stages. The first was to legally declare Ian and myself absolute guardians of David. When that was accomplished the signing of the adoption papers could go ahead. Without warning it became a matter of urgency to accomplish both steps immediately. There was to be a directive that after 14 November 1984 no adoption could be brought to court unless both adoptive parents and the child were present in Lima. For Eli and the lawyer this meant, without delay, two fourteen-hour journeys, one by bus and one by car, over a road which is no more than a dirt track and which, at one point, drops a dramatic eight thousand feet in one hour. The papers having been signed, Eli's national pride is satisfied and to her we are extremely grateful – she has our heart-felt thanks.

Two or three days before the first signing of papers we heard from Eli that, barring catastrophe, the papers would be signed and the matter concluded satisfactorily within days. Because of all the previous disappointments, however, Ian and I felt that we could not tell David until everything was absolutely definite. In preparation for the hoped-for event, Aunt May came to Rochester and on the day we were expecting the confirming phone call, David's sisters came home from university. We had also invited some friends and neighbours who have been of great moral support to us over the years that we have been fighting for the adoption. Immediately after that happy telephone call, with family and friends around him, Ian told David that the 'magic piece of paper' had finally been signed. David's look was one of surprise and embarrassment. Ian then took David's hand and said: 'The next time you come to the Clinic they will not call out David Lopez, they will call David Jackson.' At these words David's eyes filled with tears. After much hugging, kissing, and congratulating I saw that he was becoming very upset so I quietly led him away. I washed his face with cool water and he became more calm. Although his next words were a statement, there was a question in his eyes and in his voice as he said: 'I'm safe now, Mum.'

Of ultimate importance to concluding David's adoption satisfactorily was the help given to us by the wife of the President of Peru, Violeta Correa de Belaunde. Señora Belaunde fulfilled her promise of two years ago to help us with David's case, when a cable was sent, in her name, from the Presidential secretary's office to the judge in Satipo requesting that the adoption papers be accepted and signed.

On the day before we were to receive the confirming telephone call from Lima, the Cardinal of Peru, Archbishop Juan Landazuri Ricketts, arrived in Rochester for his annual medical check-up at Mayo Clinic. As soon as he knew that the first stage of the adoption was definite, he dictated a telex to Satipo expressing his interest in David's affairs and urging the judge to proceed with all possible haste. He gladly accepted my invitation to be with us that evening as we waited for the call from Peru. He gladly accepted my invitation to be with us that evening as we waited for the call from Peru.

We came uncomfortably close to the deadline of the new adoption law, but we finally did succeed and there could be no happier ending to David's story.

XIII
LETTER FROM DAVID

June, 1984

Dear Everybody,

Thank you for making my life happy! I'm going to be in fifth grade next year. I've got lots of friends at my school, my best friends are Matt and Todd. I go to soccer and I swim. Sometimes I play tennis. My mum is painting my bedroom. I've got two dogs one is called Bess and the other one is called Sunshine. I've had about sixty operations, I'm lucky because I sometimes can go out the next day after an operation. When I get out of hospital mum always spoils me. She gives me jelly and icecream. Dad is the best docter I know because he is always checking on me. Dad always says, "are you ready to go home David?" I always say "yes!" Guess what — I won a prize in Sunday sthool! The dogs are barking outside and I'm going to see what's wrong. Well that's all for now, thank you very much for helping me. I am very happy to have my nose. I hope when you see my pictures you'll like it.

love, David xxx
             ooo

XIV
IMPRESSIONS OF DAVID

I have tried to tell you about David as I know him, but when one is very close to a person it is not always possible to see him as other people do. I asked my children what they remembered of David when he arrived. Linda was fifteen at the time – this is her account:

I remember vividly the morning in February 1977 when Mum said that David was arriving that day. We already knew about the little boy in Peru as Mum and Dad had told us all about him the previous November after they had returned from their trip. It wasn't unusual for Mum to have to go to the airport to pick someone up at short notice – generally because Dad forgot to tell her until the last minute! This time, however, I had the feeling that she was just a little bit nervous. For several weeks she had been trying to raise money to fund surgery for David, but as far as I knew she had been unsuccessful. As we left for school we all wished her good luck!

My thoughts that day were muddled and I found it very difficult to concentrate on anything. This was not the first time Mum had helped Dad by taking a patient into our home. I remembered baby Gudrun best of all – she had a cleft lip and palate and she and her mother lived with us for several months. We had seen photographs of David so I knew that his poor little face in reality would be the worst I had seen. With shame I recall that my feelings of apprehension were not because I was afraid to face this little boy but because I was afraid of how my friends would react. I didn't tell anyone that he was arriving.

On my way home at the end of a day that had seemed to drag, I was feeling rather ashamed about all the jumbled feelings I had had and at that point I became apprehensive about how little David would react to us!

It seemed that Martine and David were trying to rest and Mum asked us to be as quiet as possible. As I passed their bedroom door on my way upstairs I became aware of an enormous pair of dark brown eyes regarding me solemnly – the next second they were gone and the door was shut. First I was startled and then I wanted to giggle as I realised that this was the little boy who was supposed to be resting after such a long journey. The incident was repeated as first Susan, then Sarah passed the bedroom where David was supposed to be asleep. The girls sat quietly chatting in their bedroom and, overhearing them, David's curiosity got the better of him and he went in to see them – to look at them actually! What he saw obviously pleased him and in a few minutes the girls came downstairs each holding one of his hands. Poor, pathetic, funny little David! All my turmoil, all my fears, and all my apprehension vanished right at that moment. I felt quiet and calm inside but I knew quite clearly that I wanted very much to be able to shield David. I couldn't have put into words what I was going to protect him from, but intuitively I knew, as I regarded that odd little figure dressed in bits and pieces of different-coloured clothing, that I would do everything I possibly could to help Dad and Mum take care of him.

I didn't really appreciate it then, but when I look back now I realise how tired Mum must have been. David did a lot of crying during the night. When we were around it was a lot easier because he was happy to be with us; it is almost uncanny how naturally he fitted into the family. For Susan, Sarah and myself it really wasn't too difficult to take David around with us within our own circle of friends because they were all old enough to feel sorry for a little boy who was as unfortunate as he was. It was harder for Andrew. I suppose we girls mothered David and spoiled him, and to some extent were a bit insensitive towards Andrew. I can understand now that he must have felt quite left out of things to begin with. He wasn't old enough to take David out alone and so David was much more often with us. I think also that Andrew subconsciously felt cheated when he saw David being cuddled so much by Mum. As usual, Granny knew what to do! She spent time with Andrew and David together. She played cards with them and read to them. In this way David became more used to being around Andrew and he very quickly became much more interested in playing games with him rather than taking part in – or interfering with – what we girls were doing! After this Andrew felt that he was truly a part of 'project David'. Wise Granny.

For Sarah, Susan, Andrew and me, having David in the house and part of the family just seemed natural. It was like having a new baby. He needed a lot of love and protecting but he gave a lot of love in return – so much so that many times I felt very guilty for being angry with him when he had been particularly irritating. In spite of that, or maybe because of that, I think he always knew that he was one of the family. He has always been very perceptive and he soon realised that

135

we treated him in the same way as we treated each other!

It was hard for us then to understand the many doubts that Mum and Dad had about making David a permanent member of the family. To us it seemed simple – they loved David, he loved them – why make everything more difficult by looking for problems? Seven years further on, and as an adult, I can understand very well the difficulty of making a decision such as that. It seems, though, that the decision has evolved during the passage of time and the events which have taken place. Most of all I can now understand how much Mary and Robert love David and how much they must miss him. When he was with them in Spain during the first winters we were in Minnesota we all missed him terribly.

I'll always have memories of David crying so badly when he had to have his injection before Mum took him to the hospital. I hated to hear that so I used to cover my ears with my pillow. I remember also how consistently and patiently Mum used to go over and over words, helping David to enunciate them correctly – because for him of course it was very difficult – but lots of times we got really mad because so often she would stop us and say – 'How do you expect David to speak properly when you speak so badly!'

It wasn't easy to deal with the staring, the nudges, and the giggling behind our backs, or even worse, derogatory comments made without regard for whether David could hear them or not. It still isn't easy because sometimes you just want to scream at people and ask them if they can't understand how it must feel to be David – to go through the pain of surgery time and time again and still have people stare. Learning to help David has taught us to look at other handicapped people in a more compassionate way and to speak out more about the problems these people and their families face. I think it has taught me to be a better person – I hope so.

We have all assured Mum and Dad that David will always have our love and support, not because of the problems he faces as a result of his deformity, but simply because he is our brother.

Susan was two years younger. She remembers her first sight of David:

What I saw first were his big brown eyes peeping out of the bedroom door as he watched Sarah and me. That was it – I was sunk! His eyes had in them a mixture of doubt and longing. His curiosity soon got the better of him and he came slowly and quietly into our bedroom.

When he realised that we were happy to see him he just came forward and took our hands.

I have memories of him jumping and rolling on a big orange beanbag of Linda's. Most vivid of all, though, are the memories of the way he would snatch and eat any scraps of food on our plates. Crying! I remember a lot of crying – some nights in the first weeks it seemed as though he never stopped crying at all. After his first operation, when he was so sick, we took him to our wee house on Loch Long and the whole weekend was filled with his crying. Poor little David! Worst of all was the crying early in the mornings when he had to have his injection before going to Canniesburn. That was really hard to bear – Sarah and I would always cover our ears because we hated so much to hear him.

David is a great wee boy and growing up with him has taught each one of us to look for the good inside people no matter how the outside looks. When I think of David now I don't think about the crying any more because he is always full of fun and mischief. David can always make me laugh even when I am determined to be strict with him.

Nicest of all is to see how much he loves Mum. He always lets her win if we play guessing games and he doesn't like anyone to push her under the water if we are swimming. No matter what Mum is doing you will always hear David saying – 'Do you need any help, Mum?'

Watching David's courage makes me determined to face up to my problems the way he faces his. He goes into the operating theatre knowing that the surgery might not work but the importance to him of becoming normal seems to give him the strength to face up to it. I hope that David will be as gentle as a man as he is as a little boy. I think what he has suffered makes him the kind, loving, fun little boy that he is.

Sarah too remembers David crying:

David didn't cry – he howled. We all hated to hear him crying like that but unless Mum stayed with him he just went on and on. One night when she was particularly tired I went through to his room and got into bed with him. I began to read to him and although he didn't understand me, he liked me being there. Most nights after that we could persuade him to get into bed by showing him that one of us would read to him.

As the time passed it was obvious that David trusted us but he didn't always extend that trust to other children. I remember friends coming to visit with their children and he wouldn't share his toys with them but quickly took them up and gave them to us. Knowing that he trusted us so much made us desperate to convince Mum and Dad that his home should be with us.

I have a very quick temper and it was even worse when I was younger – at that time I was only ten years old – almost the same age as David is now! There were times when David was with me in shops, when people did not try to hide their ghoulish interest in him and would make remarks which were very hurting – my temper would flare up and I would want to hurt them – physically!

My little brother has taught me to try to look for what is inside the wrapping – to pay attention only to the outside can be very deceiving. Sometimes, although the appearance can be beautiful, the inside is ugly and other times it is the opposite way round. The hundreds of adults and children in Glasgow who gave something of themselves to David, without ever having seen him, gave us a wonderful example of unselfishness. Granny always used to tell us that we would only receive if we were prepared to give. David, and lots of children like him, are prepared to give us their trust and love and if we are to have any respect for ourselves as decent human beings, hopefully we will give them ours.

Andrew was only seven in 1977 and can't now remember what he thought about David then. He still finds it difficult to put his feelings into words, but says: 'He's really a good kid, a bit of a pest at times but he's got guts!'

A family is, of course, much wider than parents and their children. It is vital if a child is to feel secure and participate fully in the family that grandparents, aunts, uncles and cousins accept him into that kind of relationship. I have already mentioned the affection and love which developed between my own mother and David. When I asked my family what they remembered of David on arrival they all mentioned the magnetism of his eyes. It was as though in compelling you to look at them the rest of his face could be forgotten. When they came to meet him for the first time their main concern was that, if the appearance of his face should cause them distress, this would not be communicated to him. Clearly the vulnerability of that small, bright-eyed boy touched them deeply. Courageous, even then, because he faced them directly, asking immediate acceptance or rejection.

It isn't possible to tell all the funny, happy or sad incidents my family remember. Although they were all closely involved with David throughout the years of surgery, their memories of him are much more of David the boy, rather than David the patient. For them he very quickly became one of the family.

They took pride in everything he did – his prowess on the football field, in the gym (few survived the contest of 'press-ups' on the living-room floor), his singing and his dancing. At family parties songs from David are well remembered – his enthusiastic rendering of 'Mull of Kintyre' and 'One Day at a Time'.

'Any father would be proud to have a son like David'. 'Lots of children do the things he does, but to do anything in public, knowing that you may be laughed at, or even treated with disgust, makes it all a lot harder'. 'What a boy – he's so good at cheating, when you play cards with him you even come to believe he didn't!' 'David is never just hungry – he's always starving!'

These are just some of the things the family said.

Aunt May has particular memories of David sitting on Granny's knee learning all the old nursery rhymes and other stories – *The Old Woman Who Swallowed a Fly* being a great favourite and one which had to be told again and again. At weekends David would sometimes stay at Granny's on a Saturday night with Jane and Philip, and May remembers how the three used to love to act out a little play she made up for them. David was always the handsome swain who saved Jane, the fair maid, from Philip, the wicked squire. She remembers mostly the marvellous days of playing at the 'Cowboy Park' with Sana and Rhona (her two dogs) and the three children, when she became 'pardner'.

David was also a frequent overnight visitor at Aunt Pat's. There was a very strict rota kept of whose bedroom he had to sleep in! Philip says, 'It seems as though he's always been our cousin so the adoption doesn't really make much difference to us. I only remember thinking his face was different when I saw him at first, after that it didn't matter'. Jane says, 'David always listened to me as much as Philip – I like that – I think David likes girls! He talks a lot of rubbish though, he's always making up stories about things that couldn't happen – just rubbish. All boys talk rubbish. I would like to be able to disco-dance like David – he's really smooth!'

Two other people made an important contribution towards David's adjustment to living in Scotland. Edward Miller, Director of Education for Strathclyde, was one of them:

One focused immediately on his eyes, not only because there was no other feature but also because the gaze was direct and challenging. 'What do you see?' the eyes demanded. 'Do you accept me as I am or are you repelled? I can give you affection; fun; trust. All you have to do is look straight into my eyes and let me know that you accept me.'

David had arrived in February and my wife Margaret met him before I did. We are old friends of the Jacksons from schooldays albeit we had lost and found touch from time to time. When we met, then as now, the years rolled back and we slipped into the easy, comfortable footholds of relationships which had begun before marriage, careers, families.

It was early March when I first saw David and met his eyes. I knew at once how Marjorie had lost her heart to the little boy from Peru. He was very small and remarkably nimble. The Jackson home had opened to him like Pandora's box and the stimulation was clearly intense. There was no mistaking the high intelligence in the mime which was a necessary substitute for inadequate language; the dexterity with which he handled the Lego and the Dinky toys we had taken along indicated excellent co-ordination of hand and eye. The affection with which he embraced the Jacksons and the trust he gave immediately to those who were their friends was moving. David had found a home he loved with a family which loved him. It was clear from his every gesture and all his activities that he intended to stay!

David was quickly demonstrative with those he trusted. He liked to kiss and be kissed – on the mouth like everyone else! He was extremely biddable, another indication of a shrewdly perceptive approach to a home in which he wished to remain.

The sequence of events which concluded our first meeting illustrated vividly the impression he created in those early days. Marjorie had decided it was time for bed – like intelligent children everywhere David had maintained a low profile as bedtime approached! He carefully collected the little toys we had brought. Placing them in the cardboard box we had used to carry them, he mimed an exquisitely graceful check that these were indeed gifts intended for him. So assured, he kissed us goodnight, tucked the box firmly under his arm and clambered upstairs to his bedroom where he stored his treasure-trove.

One of the most immediate problems facing Ian and Marjorie was financial and at that stage it was serious. While Ian and at least one of his colleagues, Mr Moos, were prepared to work without payment, the operations and the hospital care which David required were set to cost thousands of pounds.

Archbishop Winning was the first to promise financial assistance and the widely read *Evening Times* newspaper quickly launched a 'David fund'. It occurred to me that schools and colleges in the west of Scotland might well wish to encompass such a worthwhile cause within their normal programme of community projects. I wrote to them in mid-March, suggesting that any contribution should be forwarded to Archbishop Winning or the *Evening Times*.

My patch, Strathclyde, is the largest education authority in the United Kingdom, with 1123 schools, twenty-one colleges and some 422,000 pupils. It comprises half the population of Scotland. A region of dramatic contrasts, it includes some of the most breathtaking scenery and legendary islands in the world and also some of the most tragic manifestations of urban deprivation in Europe. Over centuries of vicissitudes, Glasgow and the west of Scotland earned a worldwide reputation for hospitality and warm-hearted friendliness. The response to the 'David fund' was magnificent.

The pupils of Tobermory School, Isle of Mull, were quickly off the mark; they collected and sold whelks from the seashore. Carolside Primary School in Glasgow raised £500 through a variety of educational and recreational activities which included a stage presentation in the course of their local civic week, a 'dress as you please' day and the sale of their annual anthology of prose and verse. The Rector of Clydebank High School, an influential Rotarian, contacted every Rotary Club and Inner Wheel Club in the district from 'Lochaber to Stranraer' to enlist their support. Quietly and without fuss, St John's Roman Catholic Primary School in Ayr collected the remarkable sum of £1000 within a few weeks.

By mid-April, the *Evening Times* had received £1400 and the Archdiocesan Office £16,000. The 'David fund' was closed little more than a month after it had begun. Undoubtedly much of the effort had been made by children and young people and the communities in which they lived. Archbishop Winning was 'simply overwhelmed' by their generosity and Charles Wilson, Editor of the *Evening Times*, wrote: 'the schools were magnificent'.

The question of David's education arose. It was impossible at that time to establish his correct age. Marjorie, with the help of the various tests that had been made, guessed it as being around three. Although this is young to be considering formal education, we were aware that for David there might be considerable periods of time off school because of surgery and therefore it was of the utmost importance to begin as soon as possible.

In late March I arranged for David to be assessed by one of our specialist educational psychologists. We wanted to assess his ability by noting the speed with which he would be able to perceive and solve problems. I later learned from Marjorie that David very quickly mastered the first two or three puzzles presented to him and after that the little rascal undermined the whole structure of the test by simply refusing to conform to the order in which the puzzles were presented to him! With great good humour he proceeded to rearrange them all to suit himself. The situation was confusing for our psychologist, embarrassing for Marjorie and great fun for David! Thus the subjective impressions we had formed of his intelligence, dexterity and social maturity were confirmed. Our psychologist reported that he was undoubtedly of above average intelligence; she recommended some kind of formal education.

A decision about how to structure a programme of education for David had to be made. I convened and chaired a case conference and, perhaps not surprisingly, received conflicting advice. It happens. If you bring three experts together under a professional chairperson you can expect four different conclusions.

My own view was that David's education should be undertaken by Mary Rodriguez. After a private discussion with Mary, I proceeded on that basis.

Mary is uniquely well-qualified for such an assignment. A Glasgow girl, she has an honours degree in Spanish and had been teaching at Garvel School for children with hearing difficulties. Her husband Robert is native Spanish and speaks fluent English. Mary's qualifications and teaching experience were excellent; most important of all, however, she and Robert were already deeply attached to David, and Mary was willing to be as flexible in her commitment to his education and welfare as the changing circumstances required. I arranged to transfer Mary to a nearby secondary school which she could use as a base from which to provide the individual tuition David needed both in hospital and at the Jackson house between operations.

From then until Robert's commitments took them to Spain in 1979, Mary dedicated herself to David's education and development with a single-mindedness which overcame every difficulty and obstacle. She provided me with comprehensive reports on his progress at monthly intervals and consulted, when appropriate, with specialist colleagues, but it was Mary who did the work and she did it outstandingly well. I was extremely sorry to lose her services when she and Robert returned to Spain.

As a footnote to David's short 'curriculum vitae', our most experienced educational psychologist assessed him in November 1978, some twenty-one months after his arrival in Scotland. Without knowing his chronological age it was impossible to measure his performance accurately. It was clear, however, that David was highly perceptive: he showed considerable initiative, co-ordination and flexibility of approach. The engaging personality with which he had arrived had not deserted him throughout the recurring surgical ordeals. The little boy from Peru had come a long way in every sense. On the long road which lay ahead of him he took the wholehearted and affectionate support of countless other children and their communities in Strathclyde.

Also concerned in that first year was Alice McPherson, leader of the New Kilpatrick parish church under-five playgroup:

I first heard the facts about David's arrival in this country on the radio. It was mentioned that he was approximately three to four years old and could speak no English. The news was made more interesting for me when I realised that he was coming to have surgery under the care of Ian Jackson. Although I didn't know Ian, I knew Marjorie quite well through our children – my son Gregor was in the same class as Susan.

As the months passed I heard of David's progress and knew that Marjorie was considering ways in which she could help him to meet and learn to play with children of his own age. I suggested that it might be a good idea to introduce him to this by way of the playgroup. The best idea seemed to be to bring him along with Jane, his cousin.

I told the chairman of the playgroup about my invitation to David and I assured her that I would explain a little bit about him to the children, beforehand. I told the children that he was not as lucky as they were because they all had nice faces with eyes, nose and mouth, but that David had his nose missing and part of his mouth also. I explained that he had to spend a lot of time in hospital where the doctors were trying to make his face better, and this meant that he had a lot of pain because he had to have lots of operations. I asked them to be kind to him and to try to make him happy since he was so unlucky and he was very far away from home.

I found that I was totally unprepared for the shock of how David actually looked. I remember trying to concentrate on his brightly coloured Peruvian hat instead of the unbelievable appearance of his face. Fortunately his big trusting brown eyes drew one's gaze to them. I think the other mothers who were helping me that morning felt the same inexplicable rush of emotions as I did – shock, disbelief, pity, and what I can only describe as a desperate longing to help him. The children present that morning quite naturally stared and stared. Two of the littlest ones were a bit afraid but after watching David play with the toys, not posing any threat to them, they soon forgot and continued with their own activities. The older ones were more aggressive, not in a nasty way, but they wanted to get close to see exactly what was what. Then came all the questions for which I didn't have all the answers! I repeated what I had already told them and with David actually in front of them they accepted it and made no difficulties.

I must have been very naive indeed, however, to think that there would be no repercussions to David joining us! Very quickly after it became known, I got telephone calls from two mothers who each said she felt that it would not be possible to allow her child to continue attending playgroup if David was to be there permanently. I called a committee meeting to determine what the general feeling about this matter was. For myself, I knew in my heart that I, as a mother blessed with three normal children, and as the leader of a Christian playgroup, could not exclude David.

The main worry seemed to be the effect David's deformity might have on the other children. Fairly soon, the words of a young woman, who up until then had not spoken, brought reality and a sense of shame to everyone present. She asked if we had forgotten that we were talking about a little human being and could we, having the good fortune to have normal healthy children, deny any aspect of normalcy to David who had lost such a lot? She said that giving a little compassion would cost us nothing and that we might even attain a little humility.

David joined us, and there were no further repercussions. One of the two mothers who had had misgivings at first told me that she had been shamed by her own little four-year-old boy, who, on overhearing her telling someone that she did not want him to attend playgroup if David was there, said to her, 'I need to go, Mummy, because I have to help David if anyone is nasty to him.' The other mother also returned her child and in retrospect neither one could understand why they had behaved the way they did. They were honest enough to admit their mistake.

David very quickly showed what a great little character he was. He has a lovely sense of fun – so much so that the children very quickly accepted him and did not seem to be aware of any difference. One mother told me when she had asked her daughter what the little new boy was like, she said, 'Oh he's lovely mummy, he's got a smashing duffle coat with red fluffy wool inside!' I think that those of us who were close to David, for even a little while, could never entertain vain thoughts about our appearance without remembering David and the pain and hurt which he courageously hides.

Years later in Rochester, Candy Wood, a patient of Ian's, met David. This was the first time that David had come into close contact with an adult who had endured operations similar to his. She became a friend and ally in the struggle against disfigurement:

I was in Rochester having my four-monthly check-up and tests. Marjorie Jackson had invited me to tea at their home that afternoon. Marjorie and I hadn't been talking long when David came home from school. My heart melted as I looked at this little boy who, at eight years old, had suffered more than most people in the whole of their lives.

David had heard about me, but Marjorie reminded him that I was one of his daddy's patients and that I had also had lots of operations on my face and head.

A year earlier Dr Jackson had successfully removed a large malignant tumour from the centre of my head, leaving me with only a scar down the middle of my face, and a little inequality in the level of my eyes. Months later, due to infection and complications, it was necessary for him to perform four more operations. The result of all this was to leave me with part of my forehead bone missing, an area of skin graft on the back of my head, some folds of loose skin on top of my head and above one ear – but no tumour!

David wanted to know all that had been done and when I asked him if he wanted to see how my head looked, he said that he did. He examined it very carefully and when I asked him if he thought I should let his daddy do some more work on me he said, 'Oh yes!'

It occurred to me that, although I had to deal with the physical pain and discomfort, I was so thankful to be alive that the thought of being deformed was not a big problem for me. At age thirty-one, I was secure in my faith in a loving God and in my relationship with my husband, family, and friends, and basically confident in myself. I realised how courageous this little boy of eight was!

Apart from being laughed at, stared at, and often rejected, David has had to endure great physical pain. This, I can identify with. He has had probably more than fifty operations to my six! He has had numerous bone grafts and skin grafts. After the one large skin graft I had, I was in such pain that I literally prayed to God to come and take me away. I'm glad that God does not always grant us our requests!

It might seem that the more surgery one has, the easier it would become. Wrong! The more one has, the more one knows what to expect and to dread. To me, David is remarkable. He has surgery one day and just a few days later he is back in school. I pamper myself for weeks!

Like the shepherd boy David, David Jackson has come up against his own lions, armies and Goliaths. He has touched the hearts of millions of people in his short life so far, and I am sure he will continue to do so. As for myself, I am very thankful for the opportunity of knowing him and his family.

Bamber Valley School in Rochester welcomed David when he joined them in the autumn term of 1982. His friend Todd, also now aged ten, writes:

Although I'm a new boy in Rochester this year, David and I have become very good friends. Maybe because he has been hurt by what people say about his looks he is very kind to others and knows how they feel.

Whenever we play, David tries to include others and plays fair. I trust David and that's what makes him a good friend. It seems that David should be more angry after all he's gone through. He knows he has to go through more operations but it doesn't seem to get him down.

David has helped me be thankful for all that I have and not to feel so angry when things don't go my way. I know a lot of friends feel the same too. I wish you could know David the way I do.

His fourth grade teacher, Mrs Kuecker, writes:

David has been a real inspiration to the pupils and to me by his positive attitude towards life every day. We have never heard David grumble or complain about his misfortune. He was back in school two weeks after his surgery – thankful to be there – and the other children were amazed at his courage and determination in coping with all his problems.

When David was in hospital I had long discussions in the classroom about David's wonderful outlook on life, even when his has been one of pain, suffering and many disappointments.

He is the most polite child I have ever had in my classroom – he always remembers to say please and thank you. His politeness has impressed the other children and helped them to do likewise.

David shows his concern for others and sympathises with them when they are feeling sad or unhappy. He makes sure no child is ever left out of a game – he will go over to a child standing alone and invite them to join in.

Whenever any of the pupils begin to complain or feel sorry for themselves, we think of David – he wouldn't dream of complaining – he is too happy just to be there belonging to the group!

The school librarian, Mrs Jenny Orvis, remembers meeting David:

The first day that David came to the library and we were introduced, my thoughts did not dwell on painful operations – I saw two beautiful brown eyes whose gaze looked directly at me with self-confidence, with love, and with a trust I shall never forget.

David has a great zest for living and has no self-pity. His inner strength, his soul and his heart, shines through and makes me realise that the really handicapped are those of us who have never faced the challenge that he has.

Football – soccer in American terms – is one of David's great loves. He was therefore immensely proud when he was asked to captain one of the teams in the 1983–4 season. Fred Regal is the coach who selected him. He writes:

I couldn't say exactly why I selected David as captain, but watching him during our first practices I just knew that he would do all we expected of him. Over and over during the season he proved how right my decision was. He got the job done either by his own enthusiasm or by encouraging the other members of his team. He gained the respect of his team-mates and so how he looked didn't matter. He has a great sense of humour and is often very funny – he obviously really enjoyed being with the other kids. David had to have a lot of surgery that summer and so he had to leave us before the end of the season. We really learned then what an asset he was to us. Thank God he did not forget us. As soon as he was able to move around he asked his mum to bring him to see us play – it happened to be the last game of the season. In spite of his bandages and the pain he must have had, he did his best to encourage his team. We brought him on to lead his team through the last hand-shakes of the season – his team was undefeated. David was the captain of a winning team, but more than that, he is a winner himself.

ACKNOWLEDGEMENTS

It would not have been possible for me to write David's story without the support of my husband, my children and David himself. They boosted my morale on the many occasions when my spirit flagged. As usual David's sense of fun cheered me – when waiting for me to break from writing and prepare a meal (food is the thing most often on David's mind) he would come to where I was working, put his arm around my neck and say: 'What are you saying about me now Mum? Remember – only tell them the good things!'

Without Martine there would have been no story to write and David would never have become part of our lives. She is a remarkable young woman and we are grateful for her courage, tenacity and perseverance.

We thank Air France for the humanity and generosity they showed in flying Martine and David to London completely free of charge.

We owe a great deal to British Caledonian Airways for the help they gave us when when we first began our working trips to Peru. They were responsible later for flying Martine and David from London to Glasgow free of charge. Since then their goodwill has continued and Tony Coughlan and his staff have played a great part in David's story. We appreciate greatly all their help.

We thank Fernanda and Pépé of Tierra de los Hombres for their help with David and for the way in which they dedicate themselves to taking care of other children in great need.

Our thanks also to Carlos and Elvira Navarro for their friendship, help and encouragement.

The compassion and spontaneous gesture of help from Archbishop Thomas Winning made it possible for Ian to begin the reconstruction of David's face. We appreciate greatly his efforts to begin the fund for David's treatment.

My appreciation of the dedicated care and friendship given to David and me by the nursing staff of Canniesburn Hospital, the Nuffield McAlpin Clinic and St. Mary's Hospital is immense.

We are indebted to the Nuffield Trust Foundation for their generosity in allowing David to be cared for free of charge.

Thank you to BBC Scotland for endorsing the work of Desmond Wilcox and Alex McCall on David's behalf. The concern of Desmond and Alex for David is greatly appreciated and their efforts to help us attain a legal adoption were far and above the call of duty. Jan Riddell, Alex' assistant, has become like one of the family. Throughout the making of the television documentaries and subsequent filming she made herself indispensable in terms of moral support, caring and sheer hard work. Thank you 'Auntie Jan'. To all the film crew, to Aileen Dunsmuir and Eileen Campbell, a big 'thank you' for your courtesy, caring and sense of fun.

There are many who helped directly to achieve the signing of adoption papers for David. Our appreciation of their hard work and our grateful thanks go to them.

To Señora Belaunde, wife of the President of Peru, who graciously listened to our story and having given us a promise of help wrote a letter to the court in Satipo which was of paramount importance to the signing of adoption documents.

To Cardinal Juan Landazuri Ricketts for his help and encouragement. He also wrote to the judge in Satipo, endorsing our efforts on David's behalf and requesting that the documents be signed without delay.

Words cannot express our appreciation of the work on our behalf by the adoption lawyer Norma Calderon. She too is a woman of determination and we are grateful for it.

For the national pride of Eleanor de Zuniga we give thanks! Eli took David's cause to her heart and worked unstintingly to achieve a happy ending to his story.

It is difficult to adequately thank Padre Castillo for the comfort of his quiet assurance that what we were doing was right and for all he did then and subsequently to help us achieve the adoption.

Thank you to the vice-mayor of Satipo, José Miguel Irisarri who was of tremendous help to Norma Calderon and Eli de Zuniga.

Without the friendship, encouragement and professional advice of Karen Berger, editor-in-chief of the clinical medicine division of C. V. Mosby & Co., I would probably never have got beyond the first chapter.

We are grateful also to the law firm of Lewis Silkin & Partners in London for authenticating our documents without charging legal fees.

There is no way to tell of my gratitude to my own family in Glasgow, to Mary and Robert and Mary's family. I hope that my appreciation for all they have done for us is apparent in the telling of David's story.

Finally, my thanks to Sheila Elkin for taking my manuscript and shaping it into a book.